Good Vibrations

GOOD VIBRATIONS

Suzie Hayman

First published in 1992 by
Judy Piatkus (Publishers) Ltd of
5 Windmill Street, London W1

Reprinted 1994

A catalogue record for this book is available from the British Library

ISBN 0 7499 1111 5

Designed by Sue Ryall
Illustrations by Phyllis Mahon

Set in 11/13pt Compugraphic Baskerville by
Action Typesetting, Gloucester
Printed and bound in Great Britain by
Butler & Tanner Ltd, Frome

With thanks to Gill and Judy
for taking this book seriously.
And to Vic, for not!

Contents

INTRODUCTION

There are lots of things and lots of ideas that can help you put a sparkle into your love life. Perhaps you and your partner have been together for some time. Your love may not have dimmed or grown stale, but maybe your ways of showing it have got in a rut. Or perhaps you are alone, between relationships or mourning one that is over. Perhaps disability or illness makes lovemaking less than straightforward. Perhaps you and a partner are starting out and want to make sure your loving never becomes routine or boring. Whatever your reason for wanting some hints on new things to try, or confirmation that what you've thought about *isn't* that odd, this book is for you. This book is for everyone – solo, couples, straights or gays. You don't have to be young, beautiful or physically perfect to enjoy making love.

What is sex *for*? For most people, most of the time, lovemaking has other purposes than making babies. Sex is for love. It arises out of strong feelings of affection and attraction and is a very obvious way of expressing these feelings. Sex is for personal satisfaction. It makes you feel good. Most important of all, sex is for *fun*.

Now, the problem here is that for many of us sex isn't always that much fun after all. Sex is a very private and, for some, a sacred act. The problem with privacy is that you have to keep it to yourself. And the problem with its being sacred is you're not supposed to laugh in church. Sex is meant, we feel, to be serious and quiet and rather stuffy. Sex is often something we have had to muddle along with, doing what comes naturally and finding that this *seldom* comes naturally at all!

If you think sex is something serious and sacred, and this leaves you happy and satisfied, of course that is your privilege. But this point of view doesn't suit everyone. Most of us would like it to be more relaxed and more joyful.

To talk about the need for fun in a sexual relationship is not to trivialise it. Having fun in bed does not mean being irresponsible or taking vows and commitments lightly. My own personal view is that sex is best within a relationship, and that relationships are best when they are between two people who are loyal and committed to each other for life. However, I am also of the view that I have no right to impose this idea on anyone else if their mature and considered decision is otherwise, and if their behaviour harms no one. Using, abusing or deceiving any other person for your own pleasure is unacceptable behaviour. Respect and care for your partner are vital and basic requirements for any relationship, whether it is going to last a year and a day or for the rest of your life. But if you can't laugh and *enjoy* love and come away from lovemaking feeling better than when you started, what's the point?

Sexual experimentation and diversity can be at many levels – from using the romantic additions of a candle-lit dinner and perfume, to swinging from the chandelier while beating each other with birch twigs. You don't *need* to try anything outlandish, but if you *want* to try something new, it helps to know exactly what is available and to be reassured that whatever you want to try it is not so weird that somebody, somewhere, has not tried it before. You also need to know which 'good ideas' may not be so good after all.

Good Vibrations offers an up-front guide to what you can buy, how and where to buy it, and what you can adapt from what you have at home; what actually works, why it works and how to use it; what is a con, and should be approached with a degree of cynicism; and what may be potentially harmful and should be avoided.

People tend to be fascinated by sex aids. Let's face it, most of us are fascinated by *sex*, and therefore by anything that might add variety, enjoyment and extra excitement to our loving. But very few of us like to *admit* to that fascination. Perhaps we are afraid that showing an interest suggests that our love lives are lacking in some vital ingredient that we need to spice them up. When I was researching this book, most of my friends and acquaintances wanted to hear about the various appliances and specialised clothing. They were *dying* to see the catalogues and have a go at the goods. But, like women in an expensive dress shop, most insisted they were, 'Just browsing. I'm not really going to buy – just looking.'

While being no sexual athletes, myself and my partner tried and tested *most* of the suggestions in these pages (with a few important exceptions). Information on others has been gathered by interviews with users and enthusiasts or from independent research literature. We found the ones we tried enormous fun, and some have become part of *our* love life (massage oil – yummy!)

I'm not saying that anyone *should* use sex aids. I'm not saying that everyone *does* use them. And I'm certainly not saying that if you don't want to try anything suggested in this book that you are staid, prudish or are missing anything . . . if that's what you want. What I am saying is that plenty of people *do* use sex aids, and plenty of people find them enjoyable and revealing. If you do want to give something different or something special a whirl, you won't be abnormal, unusual or weird. It's simply a matter of taste.

Suzie Hayman

1

Getting Things Going

The first, best and most basic sexual aid is *communication*. No amount of machines, clothes or oriental spices is going to make the slightest difference to your loving if you and your partner can't *talk* to each other. The sexiest part of your body lies between your ears, and if you can't use that properly you aren't going to be able to please your partner or even yourself.

This is marvellous news for those of us with less-than-perfect bodies. Because, while a man with a six-inch (15-cm) penis is *never* going to grow extra inches, or a woman with a size 14 body is highly unlikely to shrink an extra stone, cultivating your mind and developing your understanding *is* possible for all of us. All it takes is a willingness to learn.

FIRST STEPS TO COMMUNICATING

Getting your own feelings across to someone else and listening to what they have to tell you is quite a skill. You're not born with this skill, it doesn't come overnight and it can take time and effort to learn. But that doesn't mean that learning the ropes is unpleasant – and the end result will be well worthwhile! There are three steps to learning how to communicate:

1 Accept that you aren't born knowing what pleases you

As a baby, you had to discover your own body and the world around you. You probably learned fairly quickly that stroking, rubbing and twiddling various bits felt *good*. But the chances are that hands descended from on high and pushed, pulled or even slapped those inquisitive fingers away, or filled them up with teddies, rattles and other distractions.

Later on, awkward questions might have earned you a telling off or made your parents go red-faced and change the subject. So you quickly learnt that sexual feelings and sexual activity were *not* things that should be discussed out loud and that both your body and your pleasures were 'dirty'. The result of this is that many of us limit our exploration. You often don't learn what *does* excite and please you. Or if you do, you know to keep it to yourself. Young men may get into the habit of masturbating at speed. Young women may not masturbate at all, or do so in as hidden and discreet a way as possible. Neither sexes learn how to truly enjoy the sensations of physical arousal. What you learn instead is guilt and shame.

If you are going to enjoy your love life, you need to accept that we all *do* explore our own bodies and that we all *should* explore our own bodies. They are ours to discover and celebrate, after all, and staking a claim on ourselves helps us to share all the better with any partner we wish to love.

2 Accept that what pleases us is as individual as our fingerprints

We don't expect everyone to have the same tastes in food, clothes, music or even lovers. *You* like chocolate, Katharine Hamnett, Madonna and blondes, and *I* like banana yoghurt, Dior, Mozart and brunettes. That makes neither of us abnormal or unusual – just different. We all have the same bits – arms, legs, ears, lips etc – and how we react to sexual arousal is actually very similar (of that, more later). But it can be a mistake to think that because touching this, pushing that and twiddling the other gets *you* or a previous lover going, it will have the same effect on your partner. And, of course, your tastes can change. What may have been right yesterday or last year may not be as good today.

If you are going to enjoy your love life, you need to have the confidence to accept your own and your partner's tastes. Just as in many other areas, these may be very different but are nonetheless OK for that. Chocolate addicts and banana yoghurt connoisseurs *can* live and love together without either having to give up their treats!

3 Accept that you aren't born knowing what pleases your partner

Men particularly suffer from the myth that they should *know* by instinct how to give sexual satisfaction to their partners. Men often react snappily to being asked or told in bed what their partners would like them to do, or to having hands moved to the right spot. 'Don't push me around,' they say. 'Don't you think I know what I'm doing?' The problem is that so many times they don't. How could they, without asking?

Admitting that you know how you are best pleased, because you have made your own discoveries, is difficult for both sexes. Men may not want to talk about masturbating. We call someone a 'wanker', after all, when we want to say they are useless. Women may not talk about it because they aren't expected to touch themselves at all. So, suggesting your sexual partner may be able to tell you how they might best be pleased could be taken as an insult.

The idea of women pleasing themselves frightens most men. Recent studies show that most women *don't* primarily have an orgasm from ordinary intercourse. The majority of women can and do have an orgasm from masturbation, however. It's alarming and belittling to be told that she can do better for herself than you can for her. But the other side of that coin is that many men can say the same about their own sexual pleasure. The fact is that since everyone's sexual needs and responses are *so* individual and particular, the only way to please each other and be pleased is to make your own discoveries and share them. Women who masturbate and learn how to give themselves pleasure, are actually *more* likely to enjoy sex with a partner, not less.

If you are going to enjoy your love life you need to accept that you must help your partner learn what turns you on, and what turns you off; and to ask for and listen to the same information from them.

What I mean to say is . . .

You can start getting ready for a better love life even before you get down to serious loving. Your first exercise is in learning how to make your needs known and how to pick up on your partner's desires. The key word in good communication is *assertion*. Being assertive is not the same as getting your own way. People get their own way by being aggressive – laying down what they want and how they want it. Aggression is selfish.

Selfishness does have its uses, and being selfish *can* be necessary. After all, 'being selfish' is another way of saying 'being generous to yourself'. You deserve generosity as much as anyone else. There is no real value in playing the eternal martyr and always putting other people's needs and wants before your own. This only leads to resentment and misery.

Assertive behaviour is a narrow tightrope between pleasing everyone else at your expense and pleasing yourself at everyone else's expense. The aim is for you to put across your own point of view and to have it appreciated by other people, and to listen equally to theirs. Sometimes, your wishes come uppermost, and sometimes theirs will. More often, there will be a compromise that will suit everyone. If all of you are left feeling valued and considered, you are being assertive.

Try stating your feeling and needs clearly, without apology. 'Thank you but I don't feel like going out for a drink and I'd like you to have an evening in with me, on our own.' 'I'd like you to pick your clothes up, please. It really makes me feel upset when you leave them lying around.' 'I'd like you to do the washing-up tonight. I feel angry when I think you are taking me for granted and not doing your fair share.'

To get anywhere, you don't blame the other person for what they might have done or not have done. That only leads to arguments as they disagree with what you say happened. What you do is tell them how you *feel* about a situation, without placing any fault for its having happened. And you ask them, firmly and calmly, to take note of your feelings. If you want people to respond when you say you *aren't* happy, it helps if you speak up when you *are*. 'Thank you for doing the shopping. I really appreciate your doing your share.' 'It makes me feel valued when you compliment me on my cooking.'

And ask them to tell you how they feel, too. 'I feel that you aren't happy with something. Would you like to tell me what is bothering you?' If you can get into the habit of giving and taking in this way *out* of bed, you will find it that much easier when it comes to sharing more intimate needs and wants *in* bed.

UNDERSTANDING LOVEMAKING

Sexual intercourse – going the 'whole way' – is often seen as the ultimate goal in lovemaking. 'Proper' sex is full sex. Both sexes might consider lovemaking without intercourse to be childish or second best – just 'fooling around'. Self-pleasing or masturbation is generally despised and suspected. Certain types of sex play, such as using fingers, tongue or anything else to caress various parts of the body, are only expected to happen *before* the serious part of sex – intercourse.

Seeing everything else as just part of the journey towards the proper destination has quite a few drawbacks. It can make you hurry to get to the place where you think it's all happening. Which is a pity, because what goes on in the run-up influences what you find when you get there.

So often we see sex as rather hard work, or something we have to achieve results in. He has to give her an orgasm. She has to have one, for both of them to feel successful as a real man and a real woman. The joy, the ease, the fun and the relaxation of loving are vital ingredients that often go missing.

Many women never have a climax from making love with their partner. Some *do* climax, either before or after intercourse, by bringing themselves to orgasm using hands or other things. Others are satisfied by their partner's using something other than a penis to bring them off. Why is this so?

Intercourse itself is not really designed to please women. The thrusting of the penis in the vagina is very satisfying for the man. His glans – the head of the penis – is his main area of sensation. Men can be aroused by just thinking of sex or of something that excites them, but to reach orgasm, most men need to have the penis itself stimulated. Being encased in the moist, soft yet grainy, warm and often pulsating flesh of the vagina will do this admirably. But for a woman to be excited to the point of orgasm, she needs her clitoris to receive a similar type of stimulation. The difficulty here is that the range of individual response is wider for women than it is for men. Put a vagina around most penises, and most men will excite and climax. Put a penis in a vagina, and most women will not. Why not?

UNDERSTANDING THE BODY BEHIND THE EMOTIONS

To understand, it helps to realise that the sexual organs of men and women are startlingly similar. The area that will be a penis and scrotum in a boy and the female genitals, womb and ovaries in a girl start off in a developing foetus as the same type of tissue.

If a man strokes his scrotum he can have some idea of what it feels like for a woman to have her labia touched. And clitoral stimulation is very like having the glans touched. Which means that while a man might find it highly arousing to have his testes stroked and played with, he wouldn't necessarily expect satisfying love play to come from *only* touching this area. So why should we assume that a woman only needs thrusts in the vagina to do the trick? It *is* true that nerves radiate backwards from the clitoris and down through the body, sweeping round the vagina. Women *can* have the clitoris stimulated by having these nerves affected by intercourse or direct touches. Sexual excitement can make ligaments in and around the womb and vagina flex and move, passing sensations through tissue in the body. And some women report an area inside the vagina – the G-Spot – that is supposed to give exciting sensations if rubbed or pressed. The G-Spot is said to be located on the upper wall of the vagina, about 2 inches (5 cm) inside. But the fact remains that for many women stimulation of the clitoris itself is where it's at.

There are several ways to do this. The clitoris can be touched directly, or through the hood of the skin that surrounds it. This protective hood can rub against the clitoris when tugged at by movements of the penis or fingers in the vagina. And the clitoris can be pressed between the woman's pubic bone and that of her partner as they move together. Which is why many women find *some* lovemaking positions very satisfying and others less so. The angle and the pressure can make quite a difference.

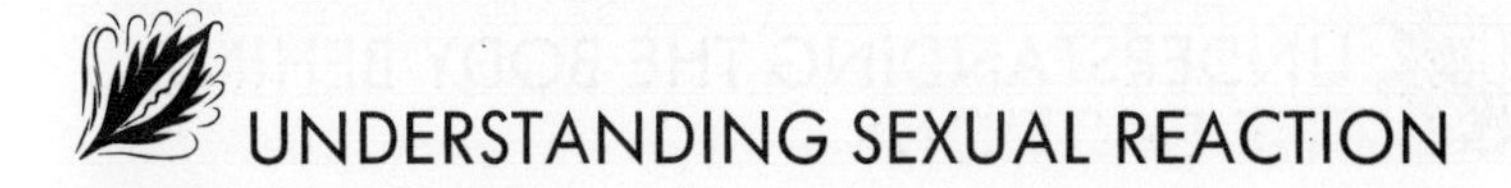

UNDERSTANDING SEXUAL REACTION

When you get excited, have a climax and then cool down, your body goes through a series of changes. There are the obvious ones – moisture in the woman's vagina and an erection in the man. But there are others, too. It may *feel* different every time, because each experience is unique. But the actual physical reactions are repeated each time you make love, and they follow the same pattern in both mèn and women. This set of reactions is called the Sexual Response Cycle, and it has four distinct phases.

Phase one is called EXCITEMENT. Men get an erection, usually within 10 to 30 seconds of being aroused. The testicles and scrotum tighten and lift up towards the body. In women, the clitoris enlarges and the inner lips – the labia minora – increase in size by as much as two to three times, and flush pink or red. The outer lips may become thinner and flatten against the body, or they may also increase in size. The vagina will produce more moisture and will become looser. Veins in the breasts may begin to fill up and show under the skin, and the darker area around the nipples will appear to spread. In both sexes, the nipples may harden and stand up.

You can stay at the EXCITEMENT stage for any length of time – minutes to hours, depending on what is happening and what you and your partner are doing. If whatever stimulated you to become excited continues – your thoughts or daydreams, a book or film, or your partner turning you on – but you don't or can't get down to *serious* action, you can stay like this for ages. It can be pleasant and exciting, or it can be frustrating or annoying. It all depends on what you expect and want. The problem for many women is that by the time they actually start making love, their partner, who may have been the one to make the first move, may be some way into EXCITEMENT. *She* may only be beginning to be aroused. This means he can move very quickly, with only a few extra caresses, into the next phase and to his conclusion, while the woman is left high and dry. The aim of good loving is not necessarily to coincide your stages of arousal or climax, but to know where you are and where your partner is. And to make sure you both get what you want.

The second stage is called PLATEAU. In men, the penis swells further, with the shaft and tip thickening. The colour of the penis may deepen. The testicles may swell to twice their resting size and be pulled quite tightly up against the area between the legs. Drops of fluid may ooze out of the penis. In women, the breasts can increase in size by a quarter. The clitoris will retreat inside its swollen foreskin and the inner lips of the vagina will deepen in colour and gape wide. The outer lips may almost disappear, or swell so much as to seem like thick curtains. The vagina will be wet and slippery, with the inner, uppermost two-thirds of its length relaxed and wide, and the entrance gently pressing closed.

In both sexes, a blush will spread over the skin, leaving it a mottled pink on the tummy, face, neck, arms, thighs and breast or chest. The pulse and blood pressure will increase, breathing will quicken and muscles in the face, shoulders and hands may twitch. This phase lasts between 30 seconds and three minutes. Once you have reached it, if you continue to be stimulated, you will go on to the third stage of ORGASM.

At ORGASM, the penis spurts semen and the vagina and inner lips will spasm. So too will the muscles surrounding the back passage. After ORGASM, follows RESOLUTION. Within 10 to 15 minutes all the changes that have taken place will fade away in reverse order. Both sexes will experience a fine film of sweat as the sexual flush fades and everything decreases in size to its resting appearance. If you become excited, but don't experience an orgasm, these changes will take 12 to 24 hours to reverse. Then, the tissues may feel swollen and aching – in the penis and especially the testicles of the man (a state often called 'blue balls') and in the vulva and breasts of the woman. It is an uncomfortable and irritating feeling, but not dangerous or damaging in any way, except to your emotions. Getting aroused and not experiencing satisfaction can leave you resentful of your partner and feeling inadequate and loveless.

That is a description of what *happens*. How it feels to you can be another matter entirely. Each person's experience of orgasm must be theirs, and theirs alone. Agony aunts are used to getting letters from people saying, 'I don't know whether I've had an orgasm – what does it feel like?' The glib answer is usually, 'If you don't know and have to ask, you probably *haven't* had one.' But is that always true? If, from the things you've heard and read, you expected an orgasm to be an explosive, violent, highly-charged experience, you might be missing something that is *your* orgasm and very different. Orgasms can be deep, peaceful and gentle, and no less orgasmic for all that.

Understanding the Sexual Response Cycle and how it feels and works in you and your partner can help you enormously in enjoying lovemaking. Sexual aids can be used in two ways. They can help you *get there*, by helping you to become aroused and then have an orgasm. Or they can help you *stay there* by enabling you to prolong the experience of lovemaking, either to let both of you get satisfaction, or to make a loving and joyful experience last even longer.

You may also be offered appliances, creams or potions with promises of making you bigger, firmer or better and so improving your sex life. Understanding how your body changes during sex may help you to tell when these claims are false.

But before you get to the *things* that could be used as sex aids, how about trying some exercises that could help get you and your partner going?

Choose a time when you know you will be undisturbed, and make yourself comfortable. You could use your favourite seat in the sitting room, but only if you know you will be left alone. Or use a bedroom, or if it is the only way you can guarantee privacy, run a bath and lock the bathroom door. Or you could do this last thing at night, in bed.

Sit or lie back and, *in your imagination*, run your hands slowly over your body. Start at your feet and work upwards. Which places do you *like* to be touched? You might come up with the obvious ones such as the genitals, lips or ears. But what about toes, behind the knees, around the back passage, the soft skin between the back passage and your vagina or scrotum? And what *kind* of touches would you like on each place? Light, feathery ones; sweeping strokes; flicking licks of the tongue? Sucking? Light scratching, hard pressure, light slaps? Would it feel better if some soap or oil was smoothed on first? Or if the hand had a covering of silk or fur, or was rough and scratchy?

There are no rights or wrongs in this exercise. And no 'normal' and 'abnormal'. What you need to do is to be honest with yourself about which parts *you* would appreciate being stimulated, and how. You might be surprised. You might discover a desire to be rougher or gentler than you have previously thought. Take your time to relax and imagine. Don't *do* anything yet, just think about it.

Having thought – act. Again arrange a time and place on your own. Undress, and lying or sitting comfortably, or standing in front of a mirror, run your hands over yourself and try out the ideas you came up with. You may feel awkward or silly, or even guilty or 'naughty', at first. Don't worry, your feelings are natural. But tell yourself that you're acting on 'Doctors orders', and it's allowed! You will probably find that touching yourself is very different from being touched by another person. Your brain is having to deal with two sensations – the part of you doing the touching as well as the part being touched. This can make the feelings *more* exciting, or it can make them confusing and less arousing. You might find that some touches are less, and some are more, sensational than you thought they would be. Use some oil, cream or soap to let your hand move more smoothly. And try touches with a hand or an object covered with a soft material. Try a feather or a comb, and see what that feels like.

You now have a chance to share some of your discoveries with your partner. It is important that you both feel free to *offer* your own discoveries and to *learn* your partner's. So begin by making a contract.

Making a contract may sound very formal. In fact, it's an exciting and important way of getting things straight from the start. When you make a contract, you both state clearly:

What you will *give*
What you would like to *accept*
What are the *limits*

Both of you should agree, and be happy about what you have agreed, before you go any further.

So the contract might be:

'I promise to tell you something I discovered I liked doing to my body.'

You may ask for something in return, such as:

'I would like you to tell me equally about something you discovered.'

Or you may ask:

'I would like you to listen without laughing at me or putting me down.'

Or you may set limits, such as:

'I would like us to do this [*then name it*] *in bed, but in the dark so you can't see my blushes.'*

Once you have agreed a contract, follow through. Turn and turn about, tell your partner what you thought you might like and what you did like, and listen to what your partner tells you. It is important to *accept* what is being said. You can laugh or gasp or comment with surprise. But don't say things that are a put-down such as 'That's disgusting' or 'You're weird' or 'Real men/women don't like that.' Tell your partner how and where you *would* like them to touch you, and listen to what they say.

The next stage is to try it out. Agree that one of you will lie back and the other will spend 20 minutes or half an hour slowly going over, stroking, pressing, caressing. The one who lies back can ask for certain areas or touches to be repeated or left alone. The trick is to praise and be positive: 'I really like it when you do that' or 'Could you stroke a little harder/lighter? Yes, that's lovely.' or 'A little further down, left a bit.'

Toss a coin for who gets to lie back first, and who does the stroking. Set an alarm clock, and when it rings, change over. Both of you will be as actively involved in either position. If you are doing the stroking, listen, feel and notice when your partner flinches or doesn't react, and what makes him or her stretch and purr like a kitten. Notice how it makes *you* feel to see them luxuriating in your attention. If you're being stroked, concentrate on what feels good and what feels better.

Now you're ready to make the most of what comes in the following chapters: a treasure chest of things and ideas that can make your lovemaking even more fun!

2

THINGS MECHANICAL

When someone mentions marital aids, sexual aids or sex toys, it is things mechanical, such as vibrators, that usually spring to mind. Mechanical sex aids intrigue the majority of us who would *like* to try something for a change. But claims made for them can be bewildering, so where should we begin?

These mechanical aids are usually offered with promises that they can excite, satisfy and develop. They may be used to pleasure yourself, pleasure your partner and prolong your performance.

This chapter looks at the many different devices, what they promise, and what they actually deliver.

VIBRATORS

Vibrators give sexual pleasure by trembling rhythmically. They run off mains electricity or batteries and come in several basic forms.

Some are shaped like a penis. These can be anything from

Ordinary vibrators

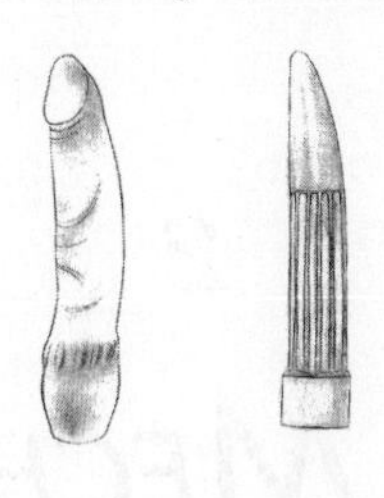

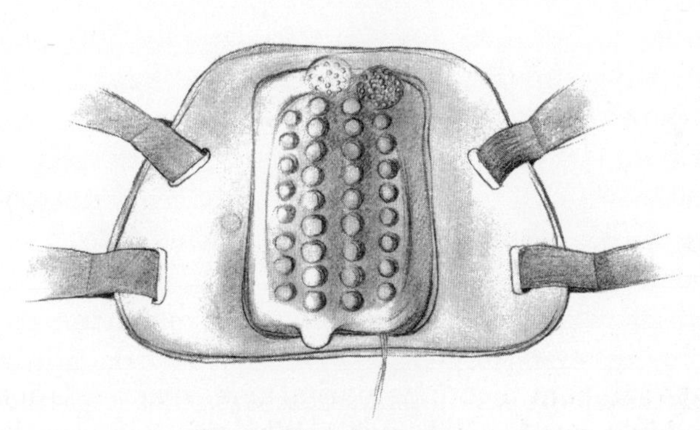

Butterfly vibrator

'slimline' (5 inches/13 cm long and 3¼ – 1 inch/2 – 3 cm in diameter) to an enormous 12 inches (31 cm) with a proportionately massive girth. Some are smooth and made of hard plastic or have a metallic finish. Some have grooves, ribbing or knobbly bumps all over them. Others are veined to look like a penis and are made of a soft latex to give a flesh-like texture. You can also get soft latex or rubber covers to transform a hard and smooth vibrator into a soft, veined one.

Some penis-shaped vibrators come with an extra bit on the base that is designed to rub against the clitoris. These may simply be small lumps or bumps, or slightly larger projections about the size of a fingernail. Or they may be several centimetres long and shaped like animals or people – beavers, elephants, dolphins, whales, penguins, kangaroos, bears, koalas or Indian braves. Some penis-shaped vibrators also contain beads beneath a soft outer skin, or have rings of beads set in the shaft. A further variation has a distinct bend at the end, supposedly to touch the G-spot, and another has a second prong to enter the back passage at the same time as the main part enters the vagina.

Penis-shaped vibrators can move from side to side, up and down, or rotate, or a combination of these. Some heat up. Some have a reservoir that can be filled with warm liquid to be squirted out like an ejaculation. And some glow in the dark.

Not all vibrators are made to resemble the penis. The 'butterfly' is an oblong pad with straps, shaped to fit against the vulva, covering the clitoris and vagina. A further variation is the size and shape of an electric toothbrush, with small, variously shaped, fitted heads. And yet another is shaped like a small egg and is connected by a cord to a separate battery pack.

All these vibrators are supposedly designed for women, for use in the vagina or on and around the clitoris. Vibrators are made for men, too. There is the ring that clips around the penis, holding a small vibrating lozenge against the base of the shaft. Others are designed as artificial vaginas. These are latex or rubber tubes, smooth on the inside or lined with soft projections. Some can 'pump up' to increase pressure around the penis. Some are plain, even clinical-looking, but others have moulded naked women dancing round the side or wrapped around, as if clinging to the penis. Some are shaped like a woman's head to simulate oral sex, and others are contained in an imitation woman's torso.

Some vibrators, while often being used for sexual excitement, are actually marketed as having other uses. Chemists and catalogues sell a 'massager' that is supposed to be for easing tension and muscular aches and pains. This can resemble a hairdryer – a pistol-shaped device with the nozzle end closed off. Various fitments can turn the business end into a smooth circular area, or one with lumps and bumps of various sizes and textures. Another variation is an oblong box which fits on the hand and makes the hand tremble.

How do they work and how do you use them?

The vibrator trembles. The vibrations, when the device is pressed against the body, can be very arousing. Some have one steady speed, while others can be adjusted from a gentle tremor to a powerful throbbing. You or your partner, on your own or together, can press the vibrator against whatever part of the body you wish to be stimulated.

The catalogues usually suggest women should use a penis-shaped vibrator by putting it inside the vagina. Some come with bends in the end that are supposed to stimulate the G-spot. Whether it does or not probably depends on what exactly turns you on. In fact, most women find that putting something *in* the vagina is not their main way of getting satisfaction. If you are going to use a vibrator like a penis and insert it, you may find you need the extra slipperiness that lubricating cream or jelly can give you (see page 63).

Good and bad points

Vibrators are fun. They are also fantastically helpful for anyone wanting or needing stimulation on their own. They can give you some help in finding new 'touchy' areas, and help you if masturbation is difficult because of illness or disability. *And*, they can make you laugh – not a bad thing in bed!

However, vibrators can be noisy, which may be embarrassing if you live in a flat or are staying at a hotel with paper-thin walls.

Do take the batteries out when travelling, or you might have the embarrassment of having the customs officer give you a very knowing look as he has to search his 27th buzzing bag that day. But before getting mortified at the thought of someone knowing or suspecting the source of the noise . . . if they recognise it, the odds are they have one too.

Do keep spare batteries handy for a battery-powered vibrator. There's nothing quite as annoying as running flat at that vital moment. If you use a mains-operated one, resist the temptation to ring up and scream at your electricity company at the eleventh blackout this winter. They will have enough problems already and might not share your ideas on what constitutes an emergency!

Warnings

Never *ever* use a vibrator near water unless it says in the instructions that this *is* safe.

Vibrators come into close and constant contact with intimate body fluids so, if you want to keep healthy, you will pay particular attention to hygiene. Wash or clean a vibrator after you have used it, or cover it with a fresh condom each time, throwing away the used one afterwards. You should also be very careful how and with whom you share sex toys. HIV (the virus that can lead to AIDS) and other sexually transmitted infections can be passed on a vibrator as easily as they can through genital contact. If you are not 101 per cent sure about your partner's sexual health, don't share.

You do have to be careful with what you put in or near the vagina. This isn't because there is any risk of losing anything in the body through this opening. The entrance to the womb is tiny and held tightly closed, except at the end of a pregnancy.

However, objects can get stuck in the vagina. When a woman becomes sexually aroused, the top two-thirds of this passage 'balloon out', widening and setting up a surprisingly strong inward suction. The greater the arousal, the greater the expansion and the more urgent the pull. This is why it isn't merely 'purple prose' for a man to say he feels he is being 'milked' by an enthusiastic lover. The problem is that while the penis cannot become detached, a small vibrator or other object can be pulled into the vagina and wedged deep behind the pubic bone when the woman has climaxed and relaxed. Casualty doctors have sometimes needed to use forceps and even give a general anaesthetic to remove offending articles.

Games you can play

If you'd like to try a vibrator, first decide on the type. For women, butterflies are particularly good if you want to be on your own, or if your partner is happy to watch or just be with you. You could use it until a certain point – after a first orgasm, or until just before orgasm – and then remove it and have intercourse with your partner. If, because of disability, you and your partner are unable to have intercourse, a butterfly may add a dimension to your loving.

The ring-and-lozenge vibrator can be used to arouse a male partner. It can also be worn during intercourse. This, by making his penis jiggle around, adds extra movement and stimulation for both partners.

If you want to use one of the penis-shaped varieties, try this exercise. Make sure you are warm and comfortable, and start with a gentle, buzzing speed. Pass the vibrator over your body, avoiding the obvious spots such as nipples and genitals. Then do it again, pressing harder. Increase the speed and do it again.

If your partner is with you, pass the vibrator over and let them do the same to themselves. Then have your partner repeat the exercise on you. Don't worry if you find the sensations or the situation gives you a case of the giggles.

Then move on to the more obvious places. Both sexes are likely to find it exciting if the vibrator is pressed against the nipples, on ear lobes and lips, on the inside of the legs and around the back passage entrance or the lower back. Women are likely to be aroused by having the vibrator tip passed over the labia and around the clitoris. Men may like having the length of the vibrator pressed against the shaft of the penis, or the tip passed around or pressed against the glans. They may also find it stimulating to have the tip pressed against the scrotum and against the skin immediately behind it – the perineum.

Some vibrators are clearly labelled as being waterproof and can be used with soap and water or immersed. If this *is* so, you might like to make your explorations in the bath. The warmth and slipperiness of bath time can increase your pleasure.

DILDOES

Dildo is the old term for a penis substitute. Dildoes are hardly new. They are shown in ancient Babylonian sculpture, on Greek pottery and mentioned in the Bible. The word is still used to describe any penis-shaped object that is not power-driven. However some sex toy manufacturers' catalogues confusingly offer dildoes *with* power.

Dildoes often have straps, for 'Look, no hands' use. Some may also feature a hollow bulb in the artificial testicles and a channel up the centre of the 'penis'. You can fill this with liquid and squeeze it at the moment of climax. Some dildoes are double-headed – two dildoes, back to back. Others are hollow and can contain a male partner's own penis, limp or erect, inside them. Dildoes are usually made out of plastic or latex, but ancient versions made from ivory, wood or glass are sometimes found in antique shops. One early Japanese erotic manual, the *Makura Bunko*, gave instructions on making your own:

> *Pick a fine carrot. Carve her into the shape of a penis – choose the length and width that suits your vulva. Then wash it well in pure water and wrap it in rice paper. Next put into hot ashes and leave it there for a few minutes. When it is properly warmed, take it out and strip off the paper. The dildo is ready for use. It is far more delicate than the human penis.*

How do they work and how do you use them?

Some dildoes can tremble like vibrators. Others are still and can be held in the hand, or can be strapped on to the body.

You can rub a dildo against the body or insert it into the vagina or anus and move it in and out or from side to side. A hollow one with straps can be used by a man, either when he is unable to have an erection, or if he comes before his partner is satisfied. With the dildo, he can continue to move and thrust as if he is erect, and give her pleasure with this simulated intercourse. Being able to squirt a final burst of liquid into the woman may give both partners the satisfaction of finishing the act of sex 'properly'.

Women can also use a dildo between them. One of them can strap the device to herself and use it to give pleasure to her partner by acting out male/female intercourse. Or they can give equal sensation to each other, using the double-headed variety. However, penetration does not usually seem to be a feature among gay female couples. Double-headed dildoes may be used more often by male/female couples, with the woman inserting one end in herself and then using the other end to 'ride' the man in his anus. Couples may also use strap-on dildoes to get around the legal bar against anal sex or its health risks (see Chapter 10).

Good and bad points

Dildoes can be very useful in prolonging sex between a straight couple and to provide penetration in either partner, of whatever sex and gender-orientation, if this is desired.

But because a dildo is a *substitute* penis, it might be harder to see it as a toy, adding fun to your sex, rather than a device replacing something that might be missing. And if you are using a dildo when you'd rather have the real thing, it can be a disappointment.

Warnings

If you are using an ejaculating dildo, make sure the liquid used is not harmful in any way. Putting soap or disinfectant in it 'to be safe' could, in fact, kill off helpful organisms in the vagina or rectum and allow uncomfortable conditions to develop. Use plain, clean water, or even distilled water, warmed to blood heat.

Be careful of improvised dildo substitutes. Deodorant or other cosmetic bottles with smooth, rounded, penis-shaped tops might seem a cheap way of getting a dildo. But, in the throes of orgasm, the tops can come off. A hollow cap can act like the contraceptive cervical cap. This is designed to fit in place over the cervix, and stay in place by suction. After a satisfying orgasm, the inward pull from the womb can be surprisingly strong. Each time you try to knock the cap off the cervix with your finger and hook it out, the movement may pull it back to cling even tighter. If you leave anything in the vagina in the hope that it might work itself out, you can end up with a nasty infection. If something does get jammed, *don't* wait. You will have to seek help some time, and it is better to do so *before* the offending object gives you a very offensive discharge.

LOVE EGGS

Love eggs are two hollow balls joined by a cord. They can contain smaller balls or weights that can move round inside the smooth shells.

Love eggs

How do they work and how do you use them?

Put into the vagina, love eggs are supposed to bring a woman to a climax, or to keep her in a state of constant sexual arousal. The net of nerves connected to the clitoris is wide and deep, and the tissue, muscles and ligaments that surround the vagina do feed back to the clitoris. An object pressing wide the normally collapsed tube of the vagina can cause the clitoris to move against its protective hood – or indeed press it up against your clothing. The idea is to slip the love eggs inside your vagina and then go about your daily business – housework, gardening, travelling to work or even working. Jumping up and down, bending over or rocking may increase sensation as the balls shift about inside you.

Good and bad points

Some women say that the eggs are amazingly arousing, either keeping them just on the brink, or actually causing an orgasm or a series of orgasms. The writer Frank Harris tells of convincing a woman friend to try out a set of eggs. He then watched in great amusement as he gently rocked the chair she sat in, surrounded by her companions who were completely unaware of what was going on, bringing her to one eye-rolling orgasm after another.

Love eggs are small, discreet and don't need batteries. Using them regularly encourages you to flex and use the pelvic floor muscle – the muscle that surrounds the urethra, vagina and rectum. It extends from the pubic bone, in front of your clitoris, to your tailbone, behind the rectum. If this muscle becomes slack, you might find you leak urine when you run, jump, shout, sneeze or cough. You could also suffer a prolapse, when the womb slumps down into the vagina.

Regular contraction of the pelvic floor muscle keeps this area toned up. It not only keeps in your water, but can make lovemaking quite startling. You may find that you automatically 'squeeze' the muscle while the eggs are in place, because otherwise it feels as if they will fall out. So, having learnt the sensation, try contracting the muscle while making love. Your partner will feel a firm and gentle pressure along his entire shaft. This has been described as giving a man the best of masturbation during the best of vaginal sex!

However, some women say that love eggs do nothing for them, and that they merely have an irritating sensation of something in the vagina – like a tampon that is falling out. The balls can also knock against each other, making a clip-clopping sound. Your friends may start to wonder why they keep thinking horses are coming, when only *you* are!

Warning

Try to make sure that the cord attached to the eggs doesn't slide too far up into the vagina. The eggs can be a devil to get out if they slip deep inside and you can't reach the cord. *Don't* use the eggs in the rectum (see the next section on Thai beads).

Games you can play

Why not get some love eggs and try them out, at a time when you will be at home and undisturbed? If they do arouse you, be prepared to be flushed or to take action after an hour or so. If you are with a partner, do warn them before tearing their clothes off.

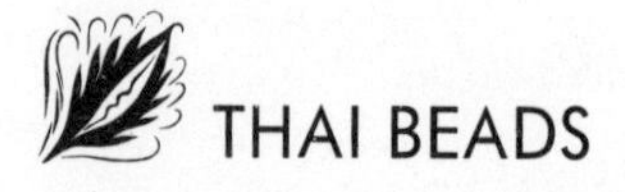

THAI BEADS

Thai beads are the anal version of love eggs. They consist of several plastic beads, either on a string, a plastic thread or flexible rod.

How do they work and how do you use them?

Having something resting in and rubbing against the sides of the rectum can be sexually arousing. As contractions at orgasm squeeze the rectum shut in both men and women, putting something into this passage can obviously excite and stimulate many people.

Beads that are on a plastic strap or rod can be gently moved in and out or flicked and vibrated during sexual arousal. All types can then be slowly, or quickly, pulled out as you climax. You can experiment and discover what speed of pulling, twisting or other motion feels best, and when you would like the beads pulled out – at the point that rectal contractions begin or earlier.

Good and bad points

Many people find the anal area extremely sensitive. Using the beads can provoke or produce particularly intense orgasms in both sexes. However they can also trigger embarrassing accidents!

Warnings

Be particularly careful not to allow anal beads to come into contact with the urethra of either sex, or the woman's vagina. This is because organisms that live harmlessly – and indeed are necessary and helpful – in your back passage, *can* cause havoc if introduced into another part. The advice about hygiene, in the section on Vibrators (page 22), counts even more here.

BUTT PLUGS AND ANAL VIBRATORS

Butt plugs are solid, tappering pieces of latex or plastic some 6 – 7 inches (15 – 18 cm) long and 4½ inches (12 – 18 cm) in girth, intended for use in the back passage. They can also be made from glass, wood or even ivory. Butt plugs tend to be larger around in proportion to their length than either dildoes or vibrators. While they are cylindrical they are not usually made to look like a penis. Anal vibrators, like those intended for use in the vagina, are battery-driven. Both have a widened end plate or a longer hand grip than a dildo or vaginal vibrator, to prevent the device slipping away inside you.

How do they work and how do you use them?

When introduced into the back passage, they dilate or relax the muscles surrounding the anus, which is usually held closed. This can prepare the user for anal intercourse or allow them to practise flexing the muscles to give stimulation to themselves or a partner. They can also be used to give pleasure.

It is wise to slather the plug with lubrication – preferably KY Jelly or Durex lubricating jelly or cream. Introduce it gently at first and either leave it in place for a time or gently draw it in and out, as you wish. Some people leave the plug in place while carrying on their normal day's routine. Some small anal vibrators are designed to be used in the anus while you also have vaginal sex. The man, the woman, or both together can then be enjoying the sensations of having his penis in her vagina *and* be experiencing anal stimulation.

Good and bad points

If you are going to involve pentration of the back passage in your lovemaking, a purpose-built device is probably the best thing to use. The back passage passes uninterrupted up the body, from the anus or back passage opening, to the throat. The first part after the anus is the rectum, which, at some 8 inches (20 cm), is twice as long as the vagina. Unlike the vagina, it has no solid end and anything inserted *can* travel, and go on travelling. Casualty doctors can tell stories of vibrators – as well as all sorts of other objects – removed from deep inside the body, where they were still buzzing enthusiastically. The only sensible suggestion is to use something that cannot possibly be lost.

Bear in mind that, unlike the vagina, the anus is not designed to open wide. As long as you go gently and gradually, no harm should result. But be too enthusiastic and you could cause anal fissures, tiny splits in the skin that can be very painful and take ages to heal. You could also weaken the walls of the rectum, allowing veins to pop out, forming painful, itchy haemorrhoids or piles. A further danger from any sort of anal sex is that bacteria that live in the bowel could be carried to your urethra or vagina. If you do use a butt plug or anal vibrator, be very careful you don't allow it to touch your partner's genitals or other parts of yours. See the advice about hygiene in the section on Vibrators (page 22) and below.

Warnings

Always wash a butt plug or anal vibrator carefully after use. Use a sterilising cleanser such as Milton, and avoid strong disinfectants unless you follow this with rinsing the plug thoroughly in distilled water. You might also consider using a condom on the butt or vibrator, as a disposable protective. And never, ever share an anal device with anyone else.

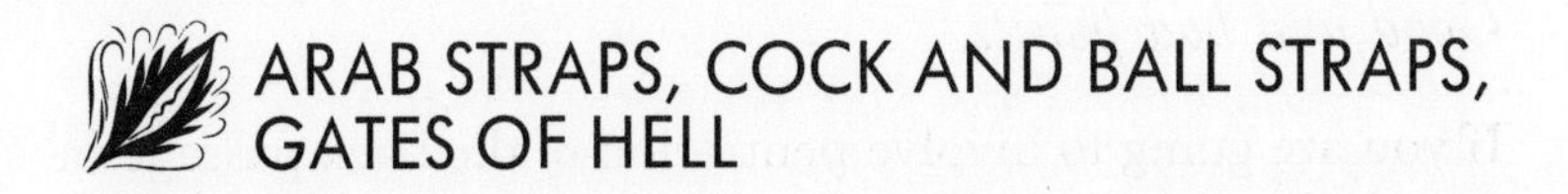

ARAB STRAPS, COCK AND BALL STRAPS, GATES OF HELL

The straps and the Gates of Hell are all devices to maintain a man's erection. They consist of rings of metal and leather, held together by leather straps or rubber bands.

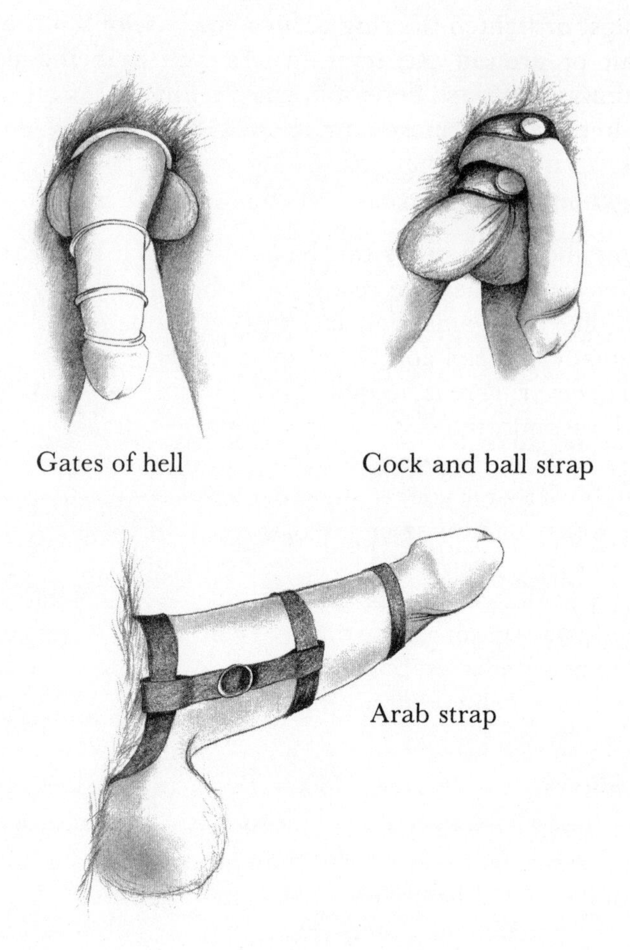

Gates of hell

Cock and ball strap

Arab strap

How do they work and how do you use them?

If you put anything tight and constricting around the penis, either when it is erect or as it swells, you can trap the blood supply inside. This effectively prevents the man from losing his erection. If several rings are worn, this may also be stimulating to the person receiving the penis, as the firm rings rub up against the sides of the vagina or rectum.

To use them, slide the rings on to the penis and fasten the

straps, or tighten the ring around the base of the penis and shaft or around the scrotum. As well as being used to maintain erection and to add sensation, straps can be a part of dressing-up games – more about those later.

Good and bad points

Some men find straps can be very useful if their erections soften before they are ready, or if they never fully harden. But, like other aids, they can also simply be fun. They look dramatic and can add visual spice to sex.

However, care is needed. These devices can be cold, hard and uncomfortable. You can't guarantee that a condom, if used, will not be snagged or damaged, so they may not be suitable if that is your method of contraception or you would like to use one for safer sex reasons. You might also like to check that if your partner has entered using a four-ring gate, he hasn't left with only three. If you lie together for some time after orgasm and he does begin to go soft, a ring can slip off as he withdraws. Some of the devices release by snapping open, so watch you don't nip a tender spot.

Warning

Don't fasten the straps too tightly or it could be painful. When using straps with a buckle fastening, remember that you have to pull it tighter before being able to slip the buckle bar out of its eye. Find out what suits you by going carefully at first, and if you *do* like them tight, perhaps get one with a stud fastening.

PENIS CORSETS AND SPECIAL CONDOMS

The corsets are lace-up, leather or rubber, open-ended coverings for the penis. Special condoms can be padded, and sometimes have straps. Some also have extensions – a solid tip in the end of the condom that can add some 3 cm to the man's length.

How do they work and how do you use them?

They are a sort of halfway house between a penis and a dildo. They can just be for show and may be used to fit over the penis and produce a sexy bulge in the trousers.

The corset can be used to keep a wobbly erection a little firmer, although the end of the penis might not be as hard and smooth as it would be with full arousal. Using padded condoms will certainly do anything a dildo can do and will allow the man to feel that it is his penis and not a mechanical device which is giving his partner pleasure. A couple may want to loveplay for a time before using a corset or special condom, and it may be a good idea to use a lubricant on the outside *and* inside for both partners to feel comfortable.

Good and bad points

If the man is having difficulty in getting or maintaining an erection long enough to have an orgasm or satisfy his partner, these devices can help. They can give the man the feeling of having far more direct involvement in satisfying his partner than a vibrator or dildo. Men who also want to lengthen their 'reach' could find them useful.

However if you are having erection difficulties, it's always best to see a doctor first, before relying on an aid. You might be ignoring an easily dealt with problem that could be important and get worse. Padded sheaths may be right for you, but don't forget that a stiff penis, or something that appears to be one, isn't always necessary for exciting sex. If penetration of vagina by penis isn't possible, consider the other options as well.

Warning

Even though they are called 'condoms', these devices are *not* intended as a method of contraception.

CLITORAL STIMULATORS

A clitoral stimulator is a plastic, rubber or latex ring, with a variety of knobs, bumps and soft projections, that slips around the penis. It is intended to rub directly against the clitoris during intercourse.

How do they work and how do you use them?

Many women find that the normal action of intercourse, with the penis thrusting in and out of the vagina, doesn't actually hit the right spot. Direct touching or rubbing of the clitoris itself may be preferred. This can be done by either partner using their fingers, or by using a clitoral stimulator. The knobs and bumps will also provide rougher vaginal stimulation, and cause sensations to pass through the surrounding tissue.

You slip the ring down the shaft of the penis so that it rests either behind the glans or at the base of the shaft. This is a matter of personal preference, and there are all sorts of shapes and designs to choose from. The woman may prefer the knobs or bumps to brush against the entrance to the vagina as the man pushes in or out, or for them to rub against the clitoris itself. It's a good idea to use plenty of lubrication cream.

Good and bad points

Clitoral stimulators are excellent aids to 'Look, no hands' sex if the woman likes direct pressure or contact on her clitoris and would also like her own or her lover's hands elsewhere at the time. They are cheap, and experimenting to find the shape or design that suits you best will not be an expensive exercise. Their use might also allow you to return to a lovemaking position that you like, but that otherwise doesn't give the right sort of sensations to the clitoris. Also, many of the clitoral stimulators give the bonus of acting as a form of erection maintainer, in much the same way as the Arab Straps and Gates of Hell.

On the other hand, clitoral stimulators can look rather fearsome, with all their spikes, knobs and twiddly bits. You might have a little initial difficulty in allowing what looks like a tiny hedgehog into such a sensitive area as the vagina. The clitoris can get very tender as orgasm approaches, so rubbing it too hard with plastic or rubber prongs can be painful. Make sure the woman has control and is allowed to direct the angle and strength of thrusts.

Warning

Most of the stimulators are tight around the penis, so care should be taken over the degree of tightness and the length of time the device is worn. Also, as they have so many knobs, bumps and spikes, you should take special care to make sure that the various crevices are perfectly clean before use.

TICKLERS

Ticklers are rubber or latex sheaths for the penis, with raised bumps and knobs on them. Some have ribs and nodules down the shaft, while others also have shapes – tentacles, fingers or animal heads – at the tip. Some are ready-lubricated, others are dry. Ticklers are often intended to be re-used after washing and are a novelty sex aid, *not* a method of contraception.

How do they work and how do you use them?

The ridges or bumps are meant to excite and stimulate the clitoris and the entrance to the vagina. The shaped ends are intended to have an effect around the end of the vagina and on the cervix. Some people find this feels exciting, others do not notice any difference. As the upper two-thirds of the vagina 'balloon out' during advanced sexual excitement, it's hard to see how any nodules at the end of the tickler could have much effect except during early lovemaking. The vault of the vagina and the cervix itself have fewer nerve endings than around the entrance to the vagina, so it could be questioned whether ticklers would have any effect.

However, many women find that their partner's climax often brings on their own orgasm – even if he has kept silent so there are no other obvious clues. In spite of not consciously being able to feel the sensation of something spurting against the cervix, his climax can still trigger hers. This may be due to a hormone in sperm that can provoke contractions. But if it is actually the sensation of liquid bursting against the cervix, a tickler might work in the same way.

The male partner can put a tickler on before any genital contact or, since you would *not* be relying on one as a method of birth control, you can withdraw and put one on during intercourse.

Good and bad points

Ticklers *can* work by providing that extra bit of friction or pressure. They can also give you a good laugh if the man has enough self-assurance not to worry if his most treasured possession looks a bit ridiculous! But they can give a false sense of security as well. Ticklers should *never* be confused with proper contraceptive condoms. They are not tested or guaranteed and should not be relied on as an effective birth control method. If a woman does enjoy the feel of ticklers, she might get the best of both worlds by using the 'ribbed' varieties of condoms that are now marketed by reputable manufacturers, such as Durex. This way, she could have that extra bit of sensation as well as the guarantee of contraceptive safety.

Warning

Do not follow the suggestion that comes with many ticklers that you should use them with a regular condom. Using more than one condom does not offer double protection – it actually *increases* the risks of bursting or tearing.

CONDOMS

Condoms – thin rubber or latex sheaths that fit over the erect penis – have three main uses. They keep things in, they keep things out and they can help a man to last longer.

How do they work and how do you use them?

Condoms will keep any sperm contained and so prevent a pregnancy. By not allowing any body fluids to come into contact with the other person, condoms can also act as a protective, stopping the free passage of any bacteria or virus.

The condom can also keep contained any cream or lotion that the man wishes to put on his penis (of that, more in Chapter 3). The thin rubber covering hardly shuts out any sensation, but it can dull it just enough to slow a quick-off-the-trigger man. This may be useful if you want to slow down lovemaking.

Either partner removes the condom carefully from its wrapper and unrolls it down the length of the penis. Condoms are easier to use if the man encourages his partner to join in 'getting it on'. Then, putting on a condom becomes part of the loveplay instead of being an interruption.

Good and bad points

Condoms are very useful for spontaneous sex. They can solve the problem of how a woman gets 'tidied up' immediately afterwards. If you like to make love outdoors or fall on each other just before going out for the evening, keeping a condom handy might be a good idea. And the recent introduction of coloured and flavoured varieties by the reputable manufacturers can make the whole thing fun. Many couples, for instance, would like to try oral sex but are put off by fears of hygiene or taste. "I won't come in your mouth" is said to be one of the big broken promises of the War of the Sexes! Using a flavoured condom can make oral sex more palatable.

However, condoms, although strong, can be torn by sharp fingernails or rings. They also still have an image of being old-fashioned sensation-killers to live down, although modern condoms are so thin that there really isn't any loss of feeling.

Some men worry about coming too soon, as a reaction to rolling the condom on. Women can find condoms difficult, too. Some say that using a condom can delay their reaching a climax, because feeling his ejaculation triggers their own orgasm.

Warnings

If you want to use a condom as a protective against pregnancy or infection, it is absolutely vital that you put it on *before* allowing the genitals to touch. It is no good starting to have intercourse, pulling out, and then putting it on.

When using condoms for contraception or safe sex, you would be wise to choose those brands bearing the 'Kite mark' and the words 'Certified to British Standard BS3704'. This isn't to say that unmarked condoms *aren't* safe. They may be, but wouldn't you rather be sure?

Certain creams or lotions and all oils will damage and dissolve condoms – often at astonishing speeds! This is particularly true of petroleum products, so Vaseline should be kept for grazed knees, and not be used as a lubricant for lovemaking. If you are using a condom for protection, only add creams which are supposed to be in close contact with them, such as Duragel or KY Jelly.

Games you can play

If you want to try condoms, try this. Get some from a pharmacy or your local supermarket. Choose a variety – colours, flavours and textures. Next time you make love, suggest to your partner to give them a go, and make a game of putting one on. Experiment with the flavours and colours. Choose a colour that goes with your favourite outfit, or a flavour that you like. Then, make a date to make love using that colour or flavour of condom the next time you wear those clothes or eat that food!

MALE DEVELOPERS

These are glass or plastic cylinders with a plastic or rubber tube and bulb attached. According to the claims, they help men increase the size of the penis and are what you will probably receive if you reply to any of the 'Watch your penis grow!' advertisements in papers or magazines.

How do they work and how do you use them?

You slip the cylinder over the penis and press it up, tight against the body. You then use the bulb and tube to pump air out of the cylinder, causing a partial vacuum. This can cause an erection. There is a battery-driven variation where the cylinder moves up and down. You can, of course, be like thousands of other men and use this unashamedly as a masturbation device. Or you can use it to start an erection and then move on to loveplay with a partner.

Good and bad points

If you are having trouble getting an erection, these devices can help – particularly if the moving variety is used with a lubricant. A developer can also help you masturbate while leaving hands free to hold a book or magazine, or fondle other parts of your body.

However, developers promise far more than they can deliver. They offer false hope to men who are convinced that their lives would change for the better if they could add an extra inch to what Nature has provided. No amount of pumping or expanding, whether by a device like this or by ordinary masturbation, will cause the penis to enlarge permanently. The advertisements and leaflets are very clever, since they only *imply* that this will happen with that 'Watch your penis grow' slogan. So you can – you can watch it through the cylinder, and it will 'gradually enlarge', but only from its normally limp state to its normally erect state. When you stop, nothing will have changed permanently.

If you want to watch a penis grow, a cheaper and just as effective way of doing it is to fill your hand with a good dollop of cream or gel and touch its owner the way he would like to be touched.

Warning

Over-enthusiastic use can damage blood vessels in the penis.

BREAST DEVELOPERS

These are cone-shaped devices that fit over the breast. They can come with a tube that attaches to a bulb that pumps out air, producing a partial vacuum. Or they can be fitted to a tap to bombard the breast with water jets. Another style is lined with knobbly bits to stimulate through massage, and is battery-driven.

How do they work and how do you use them?

They are supposed to firm up the breast and increase its size. Breast tissue floods with blood, and thus swells, during sexual arousal. Breasts can expand by as much as a quarter under *any* stimulation, whether direct or indirect.

To use one of these, you put the device over the breast, connect up the tube and simply switch on, turn on or pump out. You could use a breast developer as a sex toy, to stimulate your breasts and nipples, either on your own or as part of loveplay with a partner.

Good and bad points

A breast developer can make you feel good and can be especially effective it you are using it as a masturbatory sex toy. But don't expect anything more. Developers promise more than they can deliver. No amount of stimulation or massage will persuade a breast to stay inflated or make it grow in size permanently. The breast has no muscles, so there is nothing to 'build up' by massaging or stretching it. There is a wall of muscle *behind* the breasts and the best you can do is to exercise this (see page 73) so that the breasts have a firmer platform from which to hang.

Warning

Over-enthusiastic use of any of the developers might damage blood vessels, and you could find unsightly broken blood vessels showing through the skin.

LOVE DOLLS

Love dolls are solid latex or blow-up plastic replicas of people – usually lifesize. Some are complete bodies, and some are just the torso part.

How do they work and how do you use them?

Love dolls can come with just an open vagina, or with the back passage and mouth open as well. They are made in male and female forms. The females come in a range of colours and racial types and can have plastic or real hair. Some even contain built-in 'voice boxes' to give encouragement or praise.

They can be a joke – just something to be exhibitionist with at a stag party. But they can also be used by a couple who would like the thrill of a threesome, or of watching their partner perform with someone else . . . but who realise that introducing a real person can be risky. And, of course, they can be used if you do not have a partner but would like some extra help in acting out a fantasy of having sex with someone. Or if your partner does not want to share particular forms of sexual contact, such as anal or oral sex.

Good and bad points

Love dolls can provide a safety valve and an aid to solo sex, or allow a couple to experiment without the health or emotional risks of introducing a third party. But, for all the claims of being realistic, these dolls are unmistakably artificial. They look, feel, smell and taste of latex and plastic, not of real flesh. They also *cost*. The cheapest inflatable in the UK is around £40 and the adult bendy dolls, with adjustable 'naughty bits' and other refinements, can be nearer £800.

Warning

See the advice on hygiene in the section on Vibrators (page 22).

WATERBEDS

Waterbeds are custom-built rubber or plastic bags that come in a firm, boxed surround. The bags, filled with water, are used like a conventional mattress. They usually have a special heater which warms the liquid in cold weather.

How do they work and how do you use them?

You make love on it! Waterbeds are often sold as being ideal for bad backs or as having a soothing and sleep-inducing motion. But ask any honest waterbed owner, and they'll tell you the main bonus of using one is sexual. The water in the bed slops around, making the surface heave. If you bounce on it, a wave will surge back, and if you make love on it, the sexual thrusts are multiplied and increased by the water's motion.

Good and bad points

The motion of a waterbed can be exciting for couples with full mobility and very helpful for couples who have some difficulties with free movement. *But* all that heaving might make you heave! Before buying one, do check that the bed's motion will not make you sea-sick.

Warning

If, as a waterbed owner, you are also going to use a vibrator, make sure it is one of the waterproof kind, just in case of leaks.

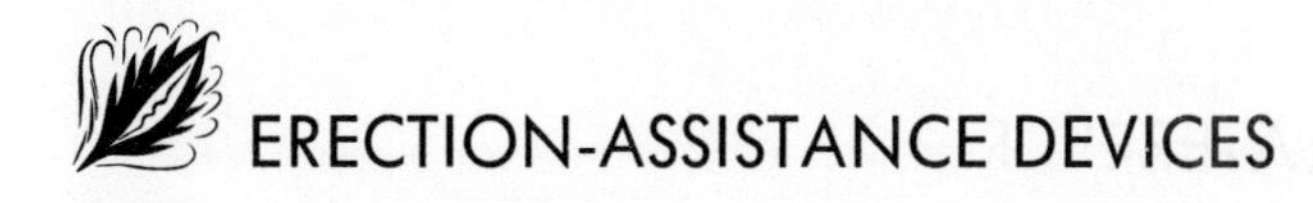

ERECTION-ASSISTANCE DEVICES

These are better-made versions of the male developers described earlier. They are intended as sex aids rather than sex toys and are designed to help a man get or keep an erection when he might have temporary or permanent difficulties in doing so.

How do they work?

There are two basic types. The first (sold under the name Correctaid in the UK) is a transparent sheath that is custom-fitted to give an airtight fit when put on the limp, lubricated penis. Air is pumped out through an attached tube. The vacuum draws the penis into the device and causes an erection. A valve in the tube is then closed and the tubing is wrapped loosely around the base of the penis. The penis remains erect, without the constriction of blood vessels, until the vacuum is released.

The second type (sold as ErecAid, in the UK) is a vacuum flask with a base seal that is put over the penis. An erection is produced by creating a vacuum in the flask. A tight, constricting band is then put round the base of the penis to maintain the erection, and the flask is removed.

Good and bad points

The makers of Correctaid claim only 10 per cent of their users are unhappy about the product and are sufficiently confident to offer a refund if it is returned within 30 days. If you are lucky, have a sympathetic doctor and are in the right NHS area, you might be able to get one free from your local hospital.

The Correctaid sheath will dull sensation for both partners. There is, however, an advantage to this. It can allow longer lovemaking and, since the device keeps an erection going, intercourse can go on, if wished, after the man has reached his climax.

Then again, these are serious products, not toys, and are made to far higher standards than the 'fun' male developers. This is reflected in their price (both types cost over £200 in the UK). However, the makers of Correctaid claim that with simple soap and water washing after use and correct storage, their product will last two to three years.

Warning

There are possible perils in trapping blood in the penis in this way. It is strongly suggested that you take a doctor's advice before considering the ErecAid type of aid.

HOME HELPS

Most of the items described in this chapter have to be bought from a shop or through catalogues. But before you reach for your purse or wallet, have a look around your home and see what you can use for free. You don't, for example, have to buy a vibrator to discover if the shakes and trembles do anything for your love life. People have been improvising these for years, using more 'innocent' devices such as electric toothbrushes or razors. All you have to do is to be careful of the bristles (although you might find this stimulating) and make sure the guard stays on the razor head.

But go carefully. They aren't exactly designed for this use and you would be most unwise to insert any part of them into your own or your partner's body. You would also get no redress if you damaged yourself, and I don't think the manufacturer's warranty would cover any damage to the goods!

Sitting on the washing machine when it goes into its spin cycle, or leaning on a hot tumble-drier are other ways of getting excited. Try sitting on the top, pulling your partner close and wrapping your legs round their body – a fine way to chase away the wash day blues! Or lean on it, face inward, and let your partner embrace you from behind.

If you have a coffee grinder or small liquidiser, you have a hand-held vibrator, but note that the motors in these are often only intended to be used in short bursts of a minute or so. Long, continuous use will burn them out. And make sure that the tops are on securely and the appliances are empty. Whirling blades are a definite sexual turn-off, and flying coffee beans, vegetables or cake mix will do nothing for your libido.

Hairdriers can be used for more than drying your head or pubic hair. A warm blast directed at nipples, penis or clitoris can get all sorts of things blowing hot and cold. Vary heat and intensity to find what you like, and don't forget that diffusers and nozzles can change the effect. *Don't*, however, be tempted to try a vacuum cleaner. The force is far too strong and can do some nasty damage.

And how are you off for bikes, teddy bears and pillows? Have you ever thought why cyclists are so fit, healthy and *happy*? It might be all that exercise and open air, but some have discovered what all those horseriders knew all along – having something between your legs that bucks and bumps when you go over the rough bits can be rather pleasant. It all depends on the terrain, and on how and on what you sit. Wearing clothing that's tight in the right spots can help. So get out and experiment. Even if you don't get amazing sensations, you'll do something about your spare tyre and make yourself fitter to enjoy other sexual activities.

Why not save yourself the money you might be tempted to spend on a dildo or a love doll and find yourself something that you already have to hug or rub against? While some people use their hands to touch breast, penis or vagina while masturbating, others press themselves against a soft or hard object. It can be the edge of a handbasin or bath, a kitchen table or a washing machine, or a favourite toy, or a pillow or mattress.

Some fruits and vegetables can make very effective dildoes. Courgettes, small cucumbers or bananas are some of the things you can use, and you might like to add a condom to protect you from hidden dirt, sharp edges or the risk of bits breaking off inside you. You could use some of these foodstuffs with a partner and have him literally 'eat you'. Mars bars were supposed to have been used by a certain 1960s pop star and his girlfriend in this way – but using the new ice-cream variety for this *might* add too much of a *frisson* for most people. Why not try it and see?

Putting chocolate-covered confectionery in the vagina could be messy, but it washes off, and any left high up should be taken care of by the vagina's self-cleaning action. However, there is a possible link in some women between extra sugars in the vagina and thrush. So use your fingers to wash thoroughly inside the vagina after this sort of sex play.

A FINAL WORD

Whether they are shop-bought or homemade, the only limits to the mechanical aids to sexual pleasure are the manufacturers' ingenuity and your imagination. You need to add common sense in their use, proper respect for the essentials of good hygiene, good manners to any partner and an awareness of good birth control. After that, all you do is – enjoy!

3
Things Chemical

Substances taken into the body – swallowed, breathed in, absorbed through the skin or otherwise delivered to the bloodstream – have been used as aphrodisiacs, to stimulate love or sexual desire, since time immemorial. Chemicals are used as *promoters*, supposedly to increase physical performance when desire is already present. They may also be taken as *enhancers*, in the hope of enlarging, or firming up, or returning to youthful potency, those parts of your body you would like to improve. Some of the substances reputed to aid sexual desire or performance are illegal and these will be discussed in another chapter.

APHRODISIACS

Aphrodisiacs are supposed to work by encouraging an erection in the man or lubrication in the woman, and feelings of heat and urgency in both. Substances taken through the mouth might actually operate as depressants, stimulants or irritants.

How do they work?

When our fears and anxieties about our bodies or our abilities as lovers put up a barrier to sexual love, a sedative can damp down those fears and quieten the imagined voices of disapproval. Anything that slows down that part of our mind that tries to stop us enjoying ourselves could be considered an aphrodisiac. These are depressants.

Tiredness and depression can also put the stops on an active love life. After all, you can't reasonably expect your body to meet the physical and emotional demands of sex if you're too tired to think straight! Any substance that peps you up can act as an aphrodisiac by making you feel livelier and sexier. These are stimulants.

Other substances may be thought to act as aphrodisiacs if, having been swallowed or rubbed on the skin, they make the genitals feel warm and itchy. These are irritants.

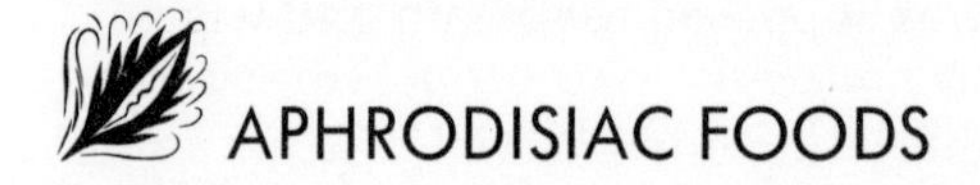

APHRODISIAC FOODS

Traditionally, a bewildering array of substances you can eat or drink is supposed to get you going. Rhinoceros horn, powdered and taken in wine or milk, is falsely supposed to increase male potency. Asparagus, bananas, eels, lampreys and ginseng are all claimed to help the man hold up his end. Female sexual desire is said to be enhanced by eating oysters, figs and marrow bone jelly.

The Perfumed Garden, an Arab treatise on the arts of love written in the sixteenth century, suggests various recipes that will, it claims, make you 'very strong for the act of love and predisposed to lying together'. Among these are mixtures of onion seeds and honey; thick honey, almonds and pine nuts; berries, oil and honey; green peas boiled with onions and spiced with cinnamon, ginger and cardamom.

The *Kama Sutra*, an even older work, was probably written

1,600 to 1,800 years ago in India. According to this book, a man can guarantee sexual ardour by drinking or eating: sweetened milk which has had a ram's or goat's testicle boiled in it; a mixture of sparrows' eggs and rice boiled in milk with butter and honey; or butter, honey, sugar, liquorice, fennel and milk. The book also suggests a drink made of galangal (a root not unlike ginger, also known as galingale), cinnamon, cloves, nutmeg, pepper, laurel seeds, thistles, cardomom, sparrow wort and gilly flowers for impotence; and nutmeg and incense mixed with honey for premature ejaculation.

Casanova recommended chocolate as an aphrodisiac, while the Elizabethans believed chestnuts, especially when mixed with spices, did the trick. In West Africa, yohimbine, obtained from the bark of the yohimbe tree, is thought to be a sexual tonic. The Koreans and Chinese believe ginseng to be a cure-all. The ginseng root looks like a man's body, with arms, legs and a penis – hence the name which means 'man root'. The English version of this is mandrake which, if dug up at the full moon, was supposed to scream and wiggle.

How do they work?

We probably think most of these foods work by sympathetic magic. Rhino horn, asparagus, eels, lampreys, bananas and ginseng are all phallic in shape. By eating them, we hope the magic will spread by contact and *his* penis will stand up and be as firm, long and vigorous as the object itself. Oysters, figs and marrow bones have the smell or appearance of a woman's vulva or vagina when she is aroused and ready for love. Swallowing oysters and slurping on the figs or jelly, we hope our sexual parts will be similarly plump, slippery and tasty. Hot foods such as onions, ginger and peppers are probably thought to be effective because they provoke sweating and a flushed appearance – much like the sexual flush. And indulgent and enjoyable tastes such as spices, herbs, sweetmeats, honey and sugar put us in a relaxed and pampered frame of mind, ready for love.

Good and bad points

Aphrodisiac foods *could* spice up your love life by forming part of a healthy, balanced diet. Plenty of fish and fresh fruit and vegetables would have a genuine effect on your well-being and thus on your sexual interest and abilities. But it has to be admitted that sharing a nut cutlet and a calorie-counted salad can't match the suggestive powers of slurping a dozen oysters together before climbing between the sheets. The general rule with all these foods or potions seems to be that if you don't need them, they could be fun. If you *do* need them, they probably won't work.

None of the foods or mixtures mentioned, however delicious or disgusting, have anything in them that could have a *specific* effect on our sexual urges. Some contain constituents that might be depressant, stimulant or irritant.

Games you can play

If you do want to try eating aphrodisiacs, you could follow some historical examples. Catherine de Medici gorged herself on artichokes, and Montezuma had pints of drinking chocolate before retiring. But Casanova's reputed use of a combination of chocolate *and* oysters is not recommended as it would probably make the bowels move before the earth did.

All in all, you might be better off just cooking a delicious, attractive and romantic meal. Choose foods you both like and that you can eat by hand. Then feed each other titbits across the table. If you want some good hints on how to make an aphrodisiac feast really go with a swing, find a video of the film *Tom Jones*, and take notes.

ALCOHOL

Alcohol is a depressant drug which affects the central nervous system – the brain and spinal cord – and so relaxes you emotionally and physically. As well as reducing anxiety and stress, and therefore increasing your confidence, alcohol causes small blood vessels to open, making you feel flushed and warm.

How do you use it?

In moderation. You could try splitting a quarter bottle of champagne between you in the bath, accompanied by a favourite nibble – smoked salmon, nuts or quails eggs. Mix the champagne half-and-half with peach juice for a Bellini (shades of Italian lovers!) or with orange juice for a Buck's Fizz (ah, those Regency beaux!)

Good and bad points

A small amount of alcohol can make you feel relaxed, happy and in the mood for sex. But more than a little, on a regular basis, will ruin your love life and a lot more besides. Drunks are *never* sexy, and even light but regular drinking can lead to impotence and many other problems. Add a dash to your love life on special occasions by all means. But if you need it and use it too often, you may soon find it ruins a good thing.

SPANISH FLY

Spanish Fly is a powder made from dried Lytta Vesicatoria beetles and is often offered for sale as a specific sex aid.

How does it work?

The active ingredient is cantharidin which acts on the bladder and the urethra by irritating and inflaming them. Spanish Fly might be offered as a powder to add to food or drink, as a ready-mixed solution with alcohol, or as a tablet. It is taken by mouth and is supposed to result in an exciting heating up of the sexual organs that makes you insatiable in your desire for sex.

Warning

Cantharidin damages the lining of the urinary tract. Far from being a pleasant warmth, the resulting inflammation is painful and can be dangerous.

Men have died as a result of using Spanish Fly and many people have been temporarily or permanently damaged by it. DO NOT USE.

SEX PILLS, SEX SUGAR, CASANOVA TABLETS

These suggestively named but largely harmless mixtures of various sugars, colourings, flavourings, herbs, vitamins and minerals are offered for sale as specific sex aids. You are supposed to take the tablets or powders regularly, or just before having sex.

How do they work?

Mostly by suggestion. Many of these preparations contain sugar, caffeine and alcohol, which might give you a quick 'lift' but, on the whole, they are very unlikely to have any real effect. Some of these tablets are no more than multi-vitamin preparations. If taken regularly, as suggested, they might have some beneficial effect . . . *if* you were already deficient in the vitamins or minerals they were replacing. If so, you would be far better off simply eating a healthy, balanced diet.

Good and bad points

As long as you are both aware that these items have very little real value, they could be fun to use as a way of saying 'Tonight's the night!'

The only real drawback is cost. Potions and pills offered as sex aids tend to be priced far higher than the same products bought from a healthfood shop or pharmacy – and far above the same found in a proper diet. You could probably get the same effect by sticking a small brandy in your coffee and telling yourself it was a love potion.

Warning

Read the ingredients, if listed, carefully. If these potions or tablets *do* claim to contain real Spanish Fly (see pages 53 – 4), avoid them.

INCENSE

Pleasant smells have always been considered sexy. Vatsyayana, the author of the *Kama Sutra*, says a man 'should apply ointments to his body and chew betel leaves with other things that give fragrance to the mouth. His rooms should be perfumed, especially when expecting to entertain the lady of his choice'. We read in the Bible of incense and burning perfumes used to disinfect and bring fragrances to houses, and Alexander the Great sent the habit home from his military campaigns. The Roman housewife acquired it from her Greek counterpart and our own ancestors took to it with a will in the Middle Ages. The Church may then have annexed the habit, which is probably why it fell out of favour when Henry VIII launched his attack on the Roman Catholic Church. But incense has remained popular and made a real comeback in the 1960s, though it has to be admitted that it was burned at that time more as a way of disguising the tell-tale smell of cannabis!

How do you use it?

You can buy incense as sticks or cones and simply light the end. Gently blow out the flame, allowing the incense to smoulder and produce its scented smoke.

Good and bad points

Incense does smell nice, so why not buy some sticks or cones in a perfume you like? Musk, myrrh, frankincense, rose, patchouli, sandalwood and jasmine are supposed to be particularly sexy, but it's probably a matter of personal taste.

However, while being pleasant and contributing to an exotic atmosphere, there is no evidence to show that burning incense *will* increase your sex drive or performance.

PHEREMONE SPRAYS

These scents or sprays, reputed to make any member of the opposite sex irresistibly attracted to you, are offered for sale as specific sex aids. They are supposed to contain a synthetic version of the secret smells given off by men and women and are said to have a 'bees-to-honey' effect. You just spray them on, like scent or aftershave.

How do they work?

Pheremones are chemical messengers given off in our sweat. They are naturally airborne and can be inhaled. Animals use pheremones to let a member of the opposite sex know when they are ready for sex. Pheremones can be very strong and very effective over a surprisingly wide area.

Men and women certainly do respond to each other's smells, finding them sexy and appealing. But can we really make and bottle this effect? And is it really a part of so many scents, aftershaves and colognes, as manufacturers claim? In one experiment, a chair in a waiting area was sprayed with genuine male pheremones and women, given the choice, *did* choose that seat. However, this just means that they found a pheremone-scented seat more attractive than one without pheremones, all other considerations being equal. It *doesn't* mean they were driven into wild sexual passion by the spray. (None of them were observed making sexual overtures to the chair!) And if the sprayed seat had been hard and uncomfortable, while the non-smelling one had been soft, would the spray have made up for the other drawbacks?

Good and bad points

Pheremone sprays might give an otherwise shy man the confidence to charm his chosen lady. All other things being equal, a woman might choose a man using a pheremone spray over one who is not. However, in the field of human relationships, all things never *are* equal! The greatest problem about such sprays is that they may give some men the idea that they can attract women even if they neglect their hygiene, forget about their appearance and fail to make any effort to be charming, sociable and good fun.

AROMATHERAPY

This is a treatment in which aromatic oils are massaged into the skin or inhaled.

Aromatherapy enthusiasts say that the substances they use – essential oils distilled from flowers, trees, herbs and fruits – are absorbed into the body. Different oils are said to have different effects. Some are supposed to help with constipation, nervous stress or rheumatism, and others are claimed to be aphrodisiac.

How does it work and how do you use it?

There can be no doubt that substances put on the skin *can* seep through into the bloodstream, depending on how long they stay in contact with the surface and the exact make-up of the chemical involved. A chemical substance that is absorbed can travel directly into the bloodstream without having to go through the stomach and liver. This means that a small amount can go a long way and have a quick effect. Some substances that might otherwise be destroyed by the body's defence systems if they had been eaten or drunk might have surprising and unexpected effects.

You can heat aromatherapy oils on a special burner or on a ring that rests on a light bulb. You then inhale the fragrance. Or you can use aromatherapy oils as part of a massage and smooth them on to the skin. You can inhale them in this way, too.

Good and bad points

Used properly, aromatherapy is harmless, if not exactly cheap. It is entirely pleasant. If you want to see if this can improve your love life, try the essential oils distilled from black pepper, cardamom, jasmine, juniper, orange blossom, patchouli, clary sage, rose, sandalwood or ylang-ylang. But remember that there is no scientific proof that essential oils have the effects claimed for them.

Warning

Essential oils are *not* supposed to be taken by mouth and should never be put on the skin undiluted. If you buy your own, make sure you also get an unscented 'carrier' oil, such as sunflower or almond oil, and mix 3 parts essential oil to 100 parts carrier oil for use as a massage oil.

PROMOTERS

These creams, sprays and pills are all supposed to improve sexual performance.

HEAT CREAMS AND SPRAYS

Lotions and potions that are meant to excite sexual interest are hardly new. Petronius, a member of the court of the Roman Emperor Nero, recommended bathing the genitals in the juice of nasturtiums and then beating them gently with nettles. The modern equivalents are rather less painful!

How do they work and how do you use them?

Heat creams and sprays contain chemicals that slightly irritate or inflame the skin surface, making it feel warm and itchy. You simply rub in or spray on and wait for results.

Good and bad points

The creams or sprays *will* warm up the areas they touch. They also require you to massage the bits you want to heat up and it's really a moot point whether it is the products or the massage and sense of anticipation that do the trick.

Then again, any surface irritant can be risky. If you have any unnoticed spots or scratches in your skin you could be in for a painful experience. It might be advisable to test run the product for adverse reactions before you try it for real in the bedroom.

Also, these creams and sprays can be expensive when bought from a sex shop or mail-order firm. Some of the pain-relieving balms or heat creams you can buy from a pharmacy will do just as well, but you *must* check the ingredients. Most of the sex shop heat creams for use on the genitals contain about 0.5 per cent of the heating ingredient – usually methyl nicotinate. Pain-relieving balms can have two to three times as much, so mix these with a hand or body lotion, and go carefully if you want to experiment. I take *no* responsibility for the reckless who decide to give Fiery Jack, chilblain cream or grandad's favourite embrocation a try!

Warning

There is always the danger that some of the 'sex heat' preparations on offer may contain *real* Spanish Fly or cantharidin, instead of just pretending to. This is supposed to make you feel hot and horny but the reality is far less erotic because the substance works by inflaming and irritating the water passage. It can be very dangerous and damaging. Don't be tempted to try it (see pages 53–4).

'POPPER' (AMYL NITRITE AND BUTYL NITRITE)

Amyl and butyl nitrite were once used to relieve the symptoms of angina, a painful spasm that occurs when blood vessels supplying the heart with oxygen suddenly contract. When, in the 1960s, you no longer needed a doctor's prescription to get them, young people, and particularly gay men, started using them. They are now often offered by sex shops and mail-order firms as a specific sex aid.

How do they work and how do you use them?

Both these drugs are inhalants and vaso-dilators – that is, you sniff them and they cause blood vessels to expand, and the heart to speed up. They have a reputation for prolonging and increasing the strength of orgasm if they are inhaled 10 to 30 seconds before climax. The effects come on during this time and can last for some 2 to 3 minutes.

Poppers come in sprays or ampoules. You spray, or break an ampoule, under your nose and breathe in as you feel climax approaching.

Good and bad points

Unlike most of the drugs that are misused for sexual purposes, poppers are not addictive. But they *can* cause dizziness, nausea, occasional loss of consciousness, stroke-like reactions, aggressiveness and an embarrassing loss of bodily control.

Warning

It isn't illegal to use poppers but it may be exceedingly foolish. Evidence seems to suggest that infection with HIV (the virus that can cause AIDS) may be linked with their use. Gay men who have anal sex and use poppers seem more likely to become infected and then go on to develop AIDS than gay men having anal sex and *not* using them. The suggestion is that poppers in some way damage the immune system. Even if you think you are unlikely to be exposed to HIV or any other sexually transmitted disease, anything that could potentially harm your immune system is obviously dangerous.

If you have had a recent head injury, or have low blood pressure or glaucoma, you are definitely at great risk if you use poppers. In my opinion, whatever the sexual thrill obtained, the risks to *anyone* are too great to be worth the experience.

'STAY-LONGER' CREAMS AND SPRAYS

These products are sold as being suitable for men who want to be 'studs' or 'stallions'. They are creams or sprays designed to delay male orgasm and to allow the man to keep an erection longer than usual.

How do they work and how do you use them?

The sprays or creams contain a small amount of local anaesthetic. They are meant to be rubbed or sprayed on to the glans and shaft of the penis 10 to 15 minutes before penetration. This will dull the sensations in the man's penis. The effects last for about 20 to 25 minutes.

Good and bad points

A surface anaesthetic obviously works, and if there is a problem with a quick-off-the-mark climax, it will slow things down. Some men have trained themselves to come quickly and then get wound up that they are 'failing' to last longer. Each time they make love, their stress and fear can make a quick orgasm happen again. Using a delay cream or spray can break this vicious circle by allowing the man to last longer. He may then get enough confidence to be able to do it without assistance in the future.

The disadvantage is that the man can't feel much until the effects of the cream or spray wear off, and making love with a frozen penis rather defeats the object of the exercise. It can also be too much of a good thing. If he grinds on for half an hour or more, his partner can be reduced to looking at the cracks in the ceiling and the result can be friction burns rather than ecstatic enjoyment.

Also, the creams or sprays offered as sex aids can be very expensive, though they contain exactly the same ingredient as those found in minor burn, teething or sore mouth remedies. Delay creams may contain a minutely higher proportion of the active ingredient – usually lignocaine – and smell less obviously medicinal. There is no doubt that smearing yourself from a bottle marked 'Rampant Sexy Animal' is more of a turn-on than misusing your child's teething gel. But is it worth the extra for the little bit of fragrance and atmosphere?

Warning

If you get it together sooner than 10 to 15 minutes after he's applied the cream or spray, it may not all have been absorbed by his body. This could mean that some of the cream or spray could rub off on to the woman, and a frigid clitoris is not exactly desirable if she is to enjoy herself to the full. If the whole point of using this cream is for him to delay long enough for her to reach her orgasm, it's obviously important to get your timing right, or use a condom to stop the anaesthetic numbing her.

LUBRICATION CREAMS AND OILS

These oils, creams and gels, sometimes scented, are sold as a specific sex aid.

How do they work and how do you use them?

They add moisture to the sexual areas or to other parts of the body and can make lovemaking more comfortable by removing friction. There are times – around or after menopause, for instance, or just before a period – when a woman might not produce enough of her own lubrication for easy penetration or comfort.

You just squeeze some out of the tube, bottle or spray, either directly on to the area you want to be moist, or on to your hand. You may need to experiment to see how much you need to use.

Good and bad points

Some extra lubrication can be a great help. When tiredness, illness or stress reduce natural lubrication, a little artificial help can let you still enjoy the comfort of lovemaking. Lubricating creams are also an essential part of using sex toys such as vibrators.

However, if you are always dry, it would be better to go for professional help to find out *why* this happens. Using these creams can hide real physical problems that need medical attention, or be a way of refusing to confront emotional upsets that are stopping your body responding by itself.

You can buy perfectly effective lubricants at your chemist – KY Jelly and Duragel are two that are widely available. But they look a bit clinical, and their smell can be medicinal and off-putting. The sex shops and mail-order firms will sell you products that look and smell better – cinnamon-scented cream or oil, and bright pink creams with exciting names. There is even one that glows in the dark. The drawback to all these fun products is that they cost much more. But you might think the extra money well spent, if only to get away from the passion-killing smells of some of the chemist shop brands.

Warning

Any oil or oil-based cream or jelly such as Vaseline, will destroy the rubber of a contraceptive diaphragm or cap or a male condom at frightening speed. So be careful what you use if those are your methods of birth control. It is safe to use them with female condoms, however.

FLAVOURED GELS AND CREAMS, EDIBLE CONDOMS AND PANTIES

Lubricant creams which are supposed to taste of cherries, strawberries or other fruit flavours, and condoms or panties of flavoured gelatine film are all sold as specific sex aids.

How do they work and how do you use them?

They are supposed to make loving 'tasty' by giving you an excuse to have oral sex. You slather various parts of your partner's body in cream, or wrap the 'clothing' round the penis or vulva, and then lick or suck it off.

Good and bad points

Flavoured novelties can make oral sex more fun. If you are not sure whether you or your partner will like the taste or smell of intimate body fluids, you can mask them with these flavours.

Unfortunately 'lick-off' creams and supposedly 'edible' condoms and panties tend to taste awful. If taste is as important to you as smell, you might find products from natural cosmetic firms more to your liking. You will find far more palatable flavours in their fruit-based creams, gels and lip salves. Or, of course, use the real thing and raid the kitchen for honey, jam, cream or fruit purées.

Warning

Please note that 'condom' is *not* used in its proper, contraceptive or protective, sense here. Edible condoms should not, by any stretch of the imagination, be considered anything but playthings.

Edible clothing becomes unbelievably sticky when moistened, which means you have to lick and suck very hard. You may have to clean your teeth to get the last bits off!

ENHANCERS

These products claim to enlarge or firm up parts of your body.

In the *Kama Sutra*, Vatsyayana promises that anointing the penis with an ointment made of various plant extracts, aubergine slices and buffalo butter, or with oil boiled with pomegranate seeds, cucumber, aubergines and juices, will cause it to swell and enlarge. *The Perfumed Garden* records several recipes for 'increasing the size of small members and making them splendid'. Rubbing the penis with tepid water will apparently do the trick. Even better, anoint it with a mixture of honey and ginger. You can add pepper, lavender, galganga (a root not unlike ginger, also known as galingale) and musk for a more exotic paste. More outlandishly, fill a jar with leeches, top up with oil, leave it in the sun to dissolve, and rub the resultant mass on to the penis!

Nowadays you may just be offered ointments supposedly containing hormones and said to be for the purpose of enlarging the penis or breasts.

How do they work and how do you use them?

You are supposed to rub the appropriate part of the body with the potion. Anything that requires you to rub the penis, vulva or breasts will cause them to engorge and swell. But, as with mechanical 'developers', the change in size will not last.

Good and bad points

Rubbing in the cream or ointment will probably feel rather nice but your hopes are likely to be the only things enlarged. Your bank balance will be the only area that will not return to its former size after use.

Warning

Sex hormones trigger changes in size and shape of sex parts during puberty. This has led to a popular belief that a dose of hormones would increase the size of adult sex organs, but it simply isn't true.

Hormones can only be obtained legally in the UK with a doctor's prescription. Any product on sale claiming to contain hormones is either misrepresented, or illegal and possibly dangerous. Taking hormones without medical advice is downright foolish.

If you feel called upon to try out any of the recipes included in *The Perfumed Garden*, please note that although the book's author, Shaykh Nefzawi, did assure his readers that all the recipes work because he had tested them, I cannot support all these promises. My male researchers took to the hills at the suggestion of leeches.

PRESCRIBED DRUGS

Some medicines prescribed by your doctor can enhance your libido or sexual desire or your ability to perform. But such treatments don't work by *giving* you potency, they work by treating a problem that is *robbing* you of sexual response. It must also be said that many drugs themselves will dampen down or destroy sexual feelings. The cure in such a case may be to discuss with your doctor the possibility of stopping taking them or having the prescription changed.

How do they work?

Drugs used to treat anxiety or depression or difficulties in sleeping – anti-depressants, tranquillisers, anti-psychotics and sleeping compounds – can all cause a loss of sexual desire in both sexes and impotence in men. Drugs used to treat high blood pressure or heart conditions – diuretics and beta blockers, for example – can do the same.

Other drugs can restore sexual feelings. For example, patients with Parkinson's Disease who are treated with levodopa may regain long-absent sexual desire and function. However, levodopa can have significant side effects and is *not* an aphrodisiac. What it does is slow down the disease process and, in some cases, allows a return to normality. Similarly, thyroxine or thyroid hormone can restore sexual feeling and ability in some people with thyroid disease or a thyroid deficiency.

A widely publicised 'cure' for sexual problems in men is testosterone, one of the male sex hormones. In cases where there is a disorder of the glands that trigger production or produce this hormone, testosterone can be given as a tablet, injection or implant. But it can lead to difficulties in passing water, abnormal (far from welcome) erections and, in some cases, to jaundice. It certainly shouldn't be given unless a deficiency has been tested for and found.

In cases where diabetes, vascular disease, spinal cord injury, pelvic injury, pelvic surgery or radiation damage has caused chronic male impotence, there are drugs that can offere some assistance. The best known perhaps is papaverine. This is injected directly into the penis and produces an erection. However, there can be serious side effects. In some cases, erections will remain, painfully, for up to and beyond 20 hours and may need surgery to relieve them. A worrying number of men have also reported scarring and lumps on their penises after use. The drug is no longer specifically licensed as a treatment for sexual problems, although it is still available (at great cost) from private clinics and doctors.

Hormone Replacement Therapy (or HRT) is often called the 'youth pill' for women. When the female sex hormone oestrogen is no longer produced because of menopause, disease or surgical removal of the ovaries, women may experience a range of unpleasant symptoms. These can include depression, loss of sexual desire and a dryness in the vagina that makes sex painful. There may also be a dangerous and dramatic thinning of the bones and an increase in the risk of heart disease. Oestrogen can reverse all these unpleasant effects. It can be given as tablets, as a skin patch, an injection, an implant, or as a cream or pessary. But again, it must be noted that giving female hormones in the form of HRT doesn't *create* desire, it simply restores it by treating the problem that may have removed it.

If you are having sexual problems and are receiving any medical treatment, check with your doctor to see if it could be spoiling your love life. Unless you ask, you often won't be told.

If you are having sexual problems and aren't on medication, see your doctor anyway. An undiagnosed illness, that may be easily treated, might be the culprit. Or it could be down to stress, emotional worries or an unhealthy lifestyle. All of these could be overcome with help from your doctor or from a counsellor.

A FINAL WORD

A healthy scepticism is probably the best attitude when it comes to aphrodisiacs. However, many things, now accepted as having both a scientific basis and a proven effect, were once scorned as quackery. And even things that only work because of wishful thinking can have their uses. But if you are offered a product with claims of dramatic and guaranteed results, look at the ingredients and the price. Could you get it cheaper? And are you sure it isn't just believing in it that makes it work?

Also, things chemical are not always things kindly, and you should be careful about what you put in your vagina – either directly or transferred from a partner. The vagina is a delicate area, so preparations that could carry bacteria are to be avoided. The vagina has its own self-cleansing mechanism and anything that upsets its balance – disinfectants, deodorants, acidic liquids or too much sugar – could result in infections or conditions such as thrush.

4
THINGS PHYSICAL

Your brain and mind may be where love and sexual desire begin, but the body is usually where the action is. There are plenty of things you can do to and with your body to enhance sexual attraction and light each other's fires.

IMPROVING IT

You can't really expect erogenous zones to tingle and erectile tissue to stand up if you are in no shape to do either. You don't have to be an Olympic athlete to enjoy lovemaking, but the fitter and healthier you are, the sexier you feel.

DIET

At any one time, a staggering number of women say they are on a diet, and nearly every woman will try to diet at some time in her life. For some of us, it is a way of life. There is always at least one book in the bestsellers' list that promises to make you slim and beautiful. Strangely, no one seems to notice that none of these books fulfil their promises. They can't, because if any of them did nobody would need to buy the next one. The truth is that crash diets don't make you slim. In fact they often make you fatter and less fit by starving you and running down your energy reserves. You lose a few pounds while keeping to the regimen, but it's pounds of muscle tissue rather than fat. As soon as you come off the diet, your body rushes to make up the lost reserves and puts on more weight – this time in the form of fat.

If you want to look and feel good permanently, don't look on diet as just a short-term option for weight loss, but as your lifetime, everyday pattern of eating. You can create easy, satisfying and delicious meals out of all the things that are good for you, and leave unhealthy, fattening items such as fat and sugar as occasional treats. Go for wholefoods – eat wholemeal (not just brown) bread, wholewheat pasta, fresh vegetables, salad and fruit, fish and chicken. Cut down on butter and full-fat cheeses. And try to cut out sweets, fizzy drinks, cakes and biscuits, fried foods, cream and full-fat milk.

It's often more effective to change your tastes than to go in for substitutes. If you use sweeteners in your coffee and tea and drink low-calorie fizzy drinks, you still maintain your sweet tooth. Switching to fresh fruit juices and unsweetened hot drinks re-educates your taste buds. You'll find you soon *prefer* sharper tastes and find sweetened foods sickly, which means you have less chance of backsliding. (Most people who lose weight by dieting gain it back again inside a year.)

EXERCISE

Some form of regular exercise will make you fitter and healthier, whatever your age, weight, sex or state of health.

Getting fit will make you more energetic. It will help your self-confidence, your self-esteem and your self-image. It will also reduce your appetite and make you feel altogether better.

If you haven't done anything active for some time, start gently and build up gradually. The aim is to do something that gets you hot, sweaty and breathing hard for around 20 minutes, three times a week. You can walk, swim, or cycle or do a keep-fit class, but make sure you do these activities properly and safely, with exercises to warm you up and cool you down to avoid any risks of injury. You may need some special shoes or other equipment, but exercise can be cheap, simple and great fun. Getting hot and sweaty with your partner is also a marvellous form of foreplay!

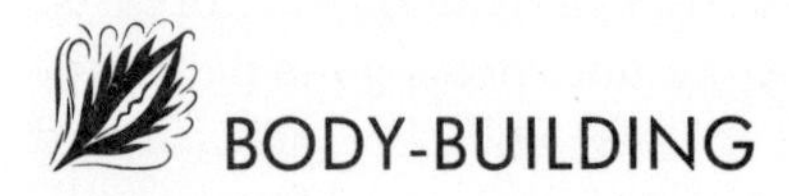

BODY-BUILDING

Getting your body in trim to please yourself and your partner is one stage. You may want to go a step further and take up body-building to mould your body into a form that excites and satisfies. Weight-training and body-conditioning can help shed fat and give men muscles while giving women a firmer outline. Women do not build muscles in the same way as men. Even at the furthest extremes of body-building, women still only show bulging masses when the muscles are under stress, as when they deliberately pose. You can train enough to give yourself a very fit, lean and firm outline and still remain totally feminine-looking. However, a surprisingly high number of men are now adjusting what they think of as sexily feminine, and the female athlete's fit body is being more sought after.

It's important to stress that while you can build up and firm up arms, legs, tums and bums, there are certain parts of the body that *can't* be altered in any way by exercise. A woman's breasts and a man's penis do not contain muscle tissue, and no amount of pumping iron is going to alter them. Breasts may even decrease in size after exercise. This is because most of their bulk is made up of fat, fibrous tissue and milk ducts. If you were overweight before taking up your exercise, it could allow you to lose some fat and these reserves of fat would melt off your breasts as much as off your hips or stomach.

You *can*, however, firm up the 'pecs' – the pectoral muscles which lie in two sheets over the ribs and underneath the breasts. Toning up these muscles gives the breasts a firmer and bulkier platform from which to hang. It also gives better posture and allows you to thrust out what you do have to better effect. Swimming can help, and if you are going to a keep-fit class or weight-training, ask your instructor for exercises for this area of your body. This is one exercise: while sitting or standing, bend your arms and bring your elbows up level with your breasts. Put your palms flat together in front of your breasts. Breathe in, and while you breathe out, press your palms together hard. Hold and count to five, and then release and breathe in. Repeat this five times, twice a day. After a week, double the number of times you do it. A second exercise is to fold your arms and grasp each arm below the elbows. Again, push inwards and count to five before relaxing. Repeat as above.

Men may, of course, find their own chests look better if they develop their pecs. But no amount of hard work in the gym is going to increase the size of the penis. This is made up of spongy tissue that increases in size when it swells with blood. There is no muscle or fat, and nothing that can become larger. Indeed, use of drugs to put on muscle bulk (see the chapter on 'Things Illegal') can actually *shrink* the size of both the penis and testicles.

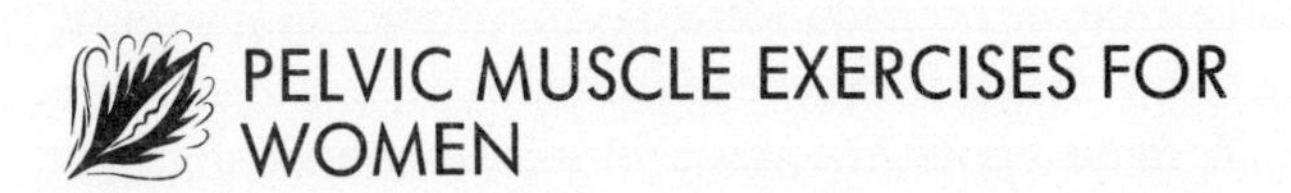

PELVIC MUSCLE EXERCISES FOR WOMEN

There is one muscle women can develop that *can* have a specific effect on their love life. As mentioned before, the

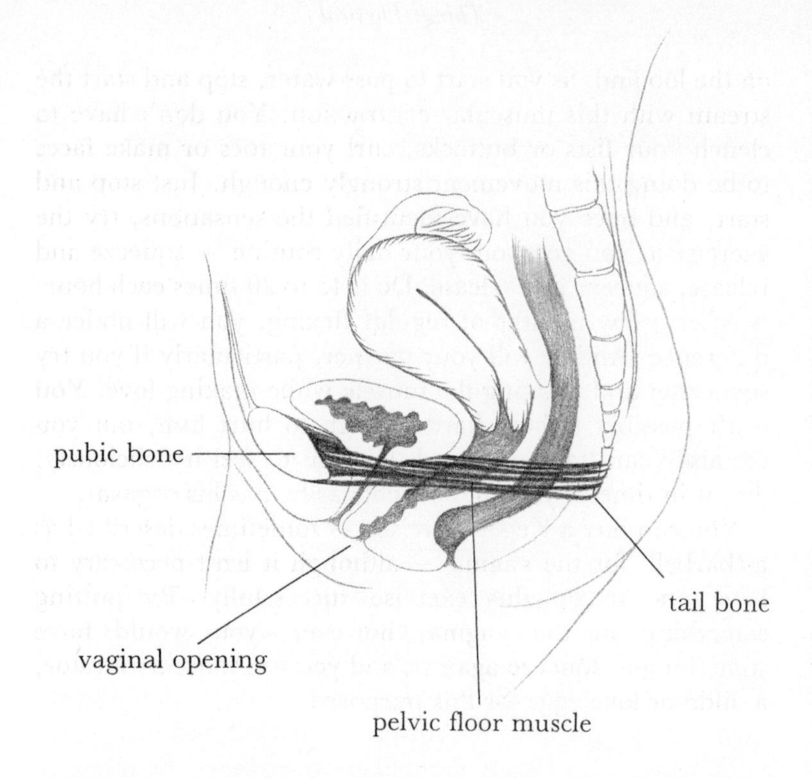

pelvic floor muscle sweeps from the pelvic bone, around the vagina, to the tailbone. It acts as a sling, supporting the pelvic organs and circling the urethra, the vagina and the back passage. If this muscle becomes slack, you may dribble a few drops of urine whenever you laugh, cough, sneeze or jump. Also, your vagina may feel loose or slack, so that both you and your partner find sex less satisfying. Eventually, the bladder or the womb may slump downwards into the vagina in a prolapse.

A gynaecologist, Arnold Kegel, identified these problems and suggested that women could avoid them by doing a set of exercises – now called Kegel exercises. You can do these at any time and in any position, with very little obvious effort.

All you need to do is pull up or draw together the muscle as if you were trying to stop the flow of urine while sitting on the loo. You can best start practising by doing just that. Sit on the loo and, as you start to pass water, stop and start the stream with this muscular contraction. You don't have to clench your fists or buttocks, curl your toes or make faces to be doing this movement strongly enough. Just stop and start, and once you have identified the sensations, try the exercise as you go about your daily routine – squeeze and release, squeeze and release. Do it 15 to 20 times each hour.

After a few months of regular flexing, you will notice a difference. And so will your partner, particularly if you try squeezing and relaxing the muscle while making love. You can't possibly tighten hard enough to hurt him, but you certainly can tighten enough for him to feel it deliciously. Try it in time to your movements as he has his orgasm.

You can buy a Kegel exerciser – sometimes described as a 'barbell' for the vagina – although it isn't necessary to have one to do this exercise successfully. By putting something in the vagina, however, you would have something to squeeze against, and you could use a vibrator, a dildo or love eggs for this purpose.

ADORNING IT

Beautifying your body can both arouse and satisfy your sexual desires or those of your partner. There are many ways you can do this – with clothing, make-up, tattoos and body jewellery.

CLOTHES

Clothes can play an enormous part in imaginative lovemaking, and in putting our sexual fantasies into action (for more on sexual fantasies, see the chapter on 'Things Fantastical'). Whether you want to enhance reality, or to transport you and your partner into make-believe, what you wear can make all the difference.

Dressing up

When sex is on the agenda, we dress to attract. If we are going out with our partner or planning an evening at home, hoping something is going to happen, we tend to choose clothes that put sex in mind and our best points forward. You might choose something that is tight or plunging in the right places, or something that has a sensuous or clinging feel to it, or that you can wriggle out of at speed. Or you may consider your partner's particular tastes. Do they happen to like you in torn jeans and a dirty T-shirt, or shorts, or keep-fit gear or evening clothes?

Both sexes enjoy the feel of sensuous material – silky, fake-fur or velvety textures. Men, too, can now wear slinky clothing; there are firms selling silk T-shirts and track suits for them (see the suppliers listed on pages 168 – 70).

Most people find underwear exciting, though it can be difficult to convince some men of the importance of this last layer of clothing. Buy him some shorts or briefs made of silk and then take them off – that should do the trick!

Clothing can also give a clear signal of what you would like to do in your lovemaking. Women can get crotchless panties – with a section missing over the vulva – allowing them to make love without removing the panties. Men can buy pants with holes in them that expose the penis while the testicles are still supported. Or there are posing pouches or thongs, which are very brief indeed. There are even elephant pants for men where the penis slips into the animal's trunk. Women can get bras with holes over the nipples, or removable panels.

You might like to buy something sexy and put it on under your other clothes next time you go out. Whisper to your partner what you are wearing halfway through the evening and see what happens!

Undressing

One fantasy that many men and women have is to see their partner taking off their clothes in a sexy and inviting way. Even if you've never thought of asking your partner to do a striptease, or done one for them, you might have realised that how we undress before making love *can* be a total turn-off . . . or add to the excitement.

The *order* in which you remove your clothes is important. The most common mistake men make is leaving socks on until last. You couldn't devise a bigger passion-killer than the sight of a naked man with an erect penis . . . and two black socks! If he simply won't change his habits, at least buy him white sports socks, as these look slightly less ridiculous.

It *can* look sexy to be half-naked with an item of clothing you would normally take off first still in place – a hat, perhaps, for a man, or a raincoat on over bra and pants for a woman. But on the whole, the order for a man should be:

- jacket or sweater
- shoes and socks
- tie and shirt
- trousers
- pants

For a woman, the order should be:

- jacket or sweater
- shoes – and tights if you wear them
- blouse
- skirt or trousers
- stockings – if you wear them
- suspenders – if you wear them
- bra
- pants

Stripping is best done slowly and sensuously, but there are

times when ripping your clothes off and throwing them down is highly arousing and very flattering, as if you just can't wait.

The point of striptease is to do just that – to strip off and to tease. Find out what your partner likes. Is it a final sight of you in your underwear? If so, reveal and then conceal, and undress slowly until you are in the state they like. Or is it a totally naked body emerging from the shirt or blouse? If so, learn to wriggle out of any underwear underneath the clothes and only discard the outer layer at the end.

If you are shy about your body, remember that your partner probably doesn't share your misgivings. A darkened room with just enough light coming through a door or curtain, or a candle or a nightlight, could make anyone feel able to show off. Or you could leave a concealing article on, but make sure it is soft and sensuous, or unusual and sexy. A silky shirt, perhaps, or a leather jacket.

Unusual clothing

What about catering *directly* for each other's fantasies? Some firms will sell you a French maid outfit to fulfil his, and perhaps her, dreams of a saucy encounter. You can buy basques which are tight-laced, or hook-and-eye corsets, that nip in the waist, display the breasts and hold up stockings. You can buy leather-look bras and pants and slinky pants for him with quick-release straps. If you want to go further and spend more, you can buy whole outfits made of leather, rubber or latex – body suits, shirts, skirts, trousers and underwear.

If you do want to try rubber or leather clothing, be warned that it demands a certain amount of commitment. Getting into a rubber outfit requires you to cover yourself and the inside of the garment in plentiful amounts of talcum powder and to pull, roll and wriggle with care into a skin-tight covering. Once in, you will sweat more than a little. This means that extracting yourself is even harder, and keeping the clothes in good condition means wiping, drying and polishing, though devotees say this is half the fun.

Considering how important clothing can be, it's a pity that many of the items sold specifically as sexual dressing by some of the larger firms involved in this field should be so sleazy, tacky, garish and badly made. If you want figure-hugging attractive items, you might be better off looking in dance and keep-fit shops or catalogues than in the sex shops or their mail-order counterparts. The exceptions here are the truly specialist small companies who cater for people with an intense interest in leather, rubber or latex wear. A number of these companies (see page 169) make bespoke clothing of the highest quality and design. Sadly, it has its price, but you might think it worth the few pounds they ask for their catalogues since most of them are beautifully illustrated with highly erotic photographs.

Many people get an extra kick from wearing clothes usually worn by the opposite sex – and their partners can also be turned on by this. This is called 'cross dressing'. You both might find it appealing if she wears his outsize shirt, or uses his tie as a belt for her jeans. You also might get a charge if he wears her underpants, or uses one of her soft silk scarves around his neck. Some couples find it exciting to go the whole hog and to dress up completely in each other clothes – suit and tie for her, and blouse, high heels, tights and make-up for him.

MAKE-UP

Archaeological evidence proves that make-up was available as early as 3000 BC. In Sumerian times, men and women painted kohl around their eyes and used red dyes on their lips and cheeks. According to the ancient Greek playwright Aristophanes, Athenian women used antimony on their eyelashes, white lead on their faces and seaweed on their eyelids. Roman women of class dyed their hair reddish-brown and smeared the grease from sheep's wool, ground deer antlers, honey and barley meal on their skin.

Upper class Egyptian ladies took face-painting so seriously that they had special cushions made on which to lean their elbows as they applied their colours. Cleopatra used black galena or lead ore on her eyebrows and painted her eyelids blue and green.

Beauty preparations are often used to give coded signals about our amatory intentions. In ancient Rome, prostitutes painted their mouths a particularly vivid shade of red to say they would have oral sex. All cosmetics, whether paint, powder or perfume, are sexual. Make-up is not designed to make you look pretty, nor does perfume try to make you smell like a flower. Cosmetics mimic the changes that take place in the human body when it becomes sexually aroused. When you are excited, your pupils enlarge, making your eyes look darker and bigger. The skin on the face flushes, especially on the cheeks and earlobes, and the lips swell and darken. The body sweats and releases a musky odour. Breasts enlarge, nipples and surrounding skin darken and engorge, and a mottled flush spreads over the whole chest area. All these changes are copied in eye shadow, mascara, blushers and lip colours.

Different cultures show their tastes by highlighting various aspects of these body changes. In India, henna is used to redden fingertips and toes, the inside of the nostrils and the earlobes – all areas affected by the sexual flush. The Egyptians used particularly vivid eye make-up, while the Cretans rouged or even gilded their nipples.

Deep down, of course, we know what cosmetics are all about. Most modern beauty firms use sexual suggestion in the marketing and packaging of their products. Put an electric motor in the average deodorant or make-up bottle and you would have a perfect ready-made vibrator. Ask yourself, for instance, why on earth we need lip colour in a *stick*? It is actually far easier to apply with a brush, from a pot. But lipsticks are phallic and much more fun to wield. Aftershaves, in contrast, sometimes come in small, squat, rounded bottles. They fit comfortably in a male palm as he fiddles with the tweakable little cap – and what does that remind you of?

To have the desired effect, cosmetics must copy the signs of sexual arousal. One way of ensuring that yours will do wonders for you is to check exactly how you look when excited. Get yourself all hot and bothered in front of a mirror and note the results. Then try to get exactly the same result with paint. The sockets of your eyes darken and the pupils widen, so use shadow and colour to achieve this look. For lips and cheeks, use a red or purple that comes as close as possible to the way your skin flushes with arousal. And don't forget that earlobes redden too – and nostrils flare. You can get this effect by using a touch of red just inside the nostrils.

For the rest of your body, notice the colouring on your breasts and nipples, and copy it with lip colour, blusher and a blue or red kohl pencil. Try a little blusher or lip paint on your fingertips and toes too – and get the colour your nails flush in nail varnish. This advice doesn't only apply to women. Sexual arousal has exactly the same effects on men and a touch of make-up can work wonders for him too.

To complete the effect, get yourself a musky perfume. Take your partner along and let him pick one out. Chances are that the scent your lover finds most appealing is the one that comes closest to your smell when turned on. Dab some on the inside of your elbows and thighs, behind the ears and knees, between your breasts and on your throat. Then dress yourself in something revealing and easy to shed.

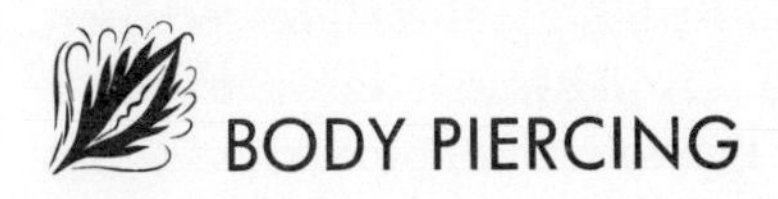

BODY PIERCING

We are all familiar with the sight of pierced ears. This type of piercing allows you to wear earrings as an attractive adornment, but many men and women find the *fact* of piercing in itself rather sexy. And others say you can use the jewellery to create pleasurable sensations. Earlobes, as we know, are sensitive, and gentle tugging, tweaking or flicking at them can be stimulating. Some people may think why stop at ears? Body piercing is becoming 'fashionable' in some circles. However, many people find it a revolting idea, and if the very thought makes you cringe, this is certainly not for you.

Ancient statues show that cultures all over the world have pierced nipples and other parts of the body for centuries. The *Kama Sutra* says that 'people of the Southern countries think that true sexual pleasure cannot be obtained without piercing the penis, and they therefore cause it to be pierced like the lobes of the ears'. Vatsyayana lists various penis enhancers that can be used to decorate the pierced organ – the 'round', the 'round on one side', the 'wooden mortar', the 'flower', the 'armlet', the 'bone of the heron', the 'goad of the elephant', the 'collection of eight balls', the 'lock of hair' and the 'place where four roads meet'.

Both men and women may now pierce ears, lower lips, noses and cheeks, nipples, navels and sexual organs.

Women can be pierced through both the inner and the outer labia, through the clitoris hood, or through the clitoris itself. The piercing through the hood or clitoris can be vertical or horizontal.

Men may be pierced through the foreskin, either in such a way as to pass a ring or barbell through to prevent the foreskin being retracted, or so that a ring can be inserted allowing the foreskin to move unimpeded. The loose bridge of flesh beneath the glans (the frenum) can also be pierced. The most popular male genital piercing is the Prince Albert. In this, a hole is made through the glans into the urethra just above the frenum. A ring is then worn that comes out of the tip of the penis and circles round underneath.

Men can also have holes pierced straight through the glans, either from side to side (an ampallang), or vertically (an apadravya). A variation is a hole just through the edge of the glans – a dydoe piercing. There is also the hafada piercing through the scrotal sac. This can be made at the side, to be visible from the front, or from underneath and behind, running in a line down the centre seam of the scrotum. Further piercings can be made at the base of the belly, just above the penis, or in the ridge of flesh behind the scrotum that lies in front of the back passage entrance – this last is known as a guiche piercing.

Why get pierced?

The most obvious reason is for adornment. If you pierce a nipple or penis, you can hang all sorts of stylish ornaments from them. But looks are not the main reason for the more 'serious' forms of body piercing. Those that have such piercings say that they contribute directly to sexual pleasure. It is said that wearing a ring or a bar through a genital or nipple piercing causes the surrounding tissue to become more sensitive and thus to give greater sensation during sexual arousal. Users also say that if the body jewellery is tugged or twiddled it can produce sexual excitement and even orgasm.

Is it safe?

Most people worry that a ring or bar worn in an intimate spot might get caught or torn out. Or that, if in a penis, clitoris or labia, it might catch and injure a partner. Users say that this does not happen and indeed report that jewellery, if felt at all, adds to their partner's sexual pleasure and sensations. Rings with a proper closure are apparently smooth enough to be used with condoms or caps, and do not damage either. However, you have to decide whether you trust what can only be opinions and statements based on anecdotal evidence. No scientific studies have been done as yet.

Having your nipples or genitals pierced is as safe or unsafe as having your ears done. That is, you would be extremely unwise to try to do it yourself and should *only* be pierced by an experienced professional. They should be registered with the local Health Authority to do such work and should use properly sterilised instruments. Proper sterilisation means that the instruments should either be correctly treated in an autoclave, not just given a quick dunk in a disinfectant, or come ready-packed in sealed units marked as being sterile.

You can now have your ears done with a disposable gun that comes ready-packed, sterilised and loaded with a stud or ring. These are *not* suitable for nipple or genital piercing; a special hollow piercing needle must be used. If proper hygiene is observed you will not be at risk of infection, but do choose your piercer carefully, with safety and hygiene in mind.

Will it hurt?

Anaesthetic sprays or gels can be used to numb the surface area, and people who have been pierced say that the experience need not be painful. Healing time can vary. Earlobe and outer labia take roughly the same time – around four to six weeks. Other parts can heal more quickly – the inner labia take one to two weeks, clitoris hood one to six weeks, clitoris one to eight weeks, Prince Alberts two to three weeks and frenums three to five weeks. However, other parts take longer – nipples, scrotal sac, navel and most glans piercings take eight weeks or more.

Like earlobe piercings, body piercings give no trouble once they are healed, according to people who have them. It may make you wince to think of a bar or ring through a nipple, or an even more tender part of your body, but the consensus is that not only does it not hurt, it feels pleasant. Obviously when choosing the part to be pierced you need to bear in mind the style of your clothing and what you do in your spare time. A guiche piercing, for example, would make cycling or horse-riding highly uncomfortable. And navel piercings could be troublesome if you tend to wear tight waistbands, as would labial or clitoral piercing if you favour tight jeans.

After healing, body jewellery can be removed and left out on occasions when the wearer feels it may alarm, distress or upset anyone – for instance, if you are going to a topless beach in a tight G-string, doing a keep-fit class in a clinging lycra bodysuit or visiting your doctor. And do remember to remove the ring or bar *before* going through airport security metal detectors. A red-faced excuse to the guard that the lights are flashing because Prince Albert is in your trousers is likely to delay your departure for quite some time!

Warning

Piercing of the genitals and other 'sexual' parts of the body is perfectly legal as long as it is being done 'for decorative purposes only'. What you do with such decorative and cosmetic additions after the event is your business. But if you are going to get a sexual kick out of the actual act of getting your body pierced, the piercer could be found in breach of the law. In a recent case, a body piercer was given a 15-month suspended sentence when the judge decided performing a piercing *for the purposes* of sexual pleasure was illegal. The piercer and client were having a sexual relationship and correspondence had been found that made it clear there were sexual overtones to the piercing. Be warned.

TATTOOS

To create these pictures or designs on the skin, special inks and needles are used so that the colours are driven under the skin surface and become permanent.

Tattoos *can* be done at home using ordinary inks and needles, but you are *not* advised to try your own hand. The results are not always attractive and are often regretted, or can lead to painful infections. Doing this with other people and sharing implements is an excellent way of passing on HIV – the virus that can cause AIDS. Modern tattoos are done with a vibrating needle, not unlike that in a sewing machine, that pricks ink into the skin at several thousand jabs a minute.

A simple and small design may only need half an hour to a few hours. A very complex or large design could take several hours of planning and a series of sessions of up to three hours each.

You can be tattooed wherever you have skin. The most obvious sites, because they are the ones we notice most, are hands, arms, chests and necks. Tattoos intended as sexual adornment are more often found on buttocks, breasts, the lower belly and on the genitals themselves – on the penis or the pubic mound. Many people take a delight in having a tattoo – small and discreet or full-blown and gaudy – in a place that only their partner will see. Of course, now that both men and women wear only brief costumes on the beach, there isn't a lot of space left that can be kept for private eyes only, which makes such 'secret' pictures all the more intimate and sexually exciting.

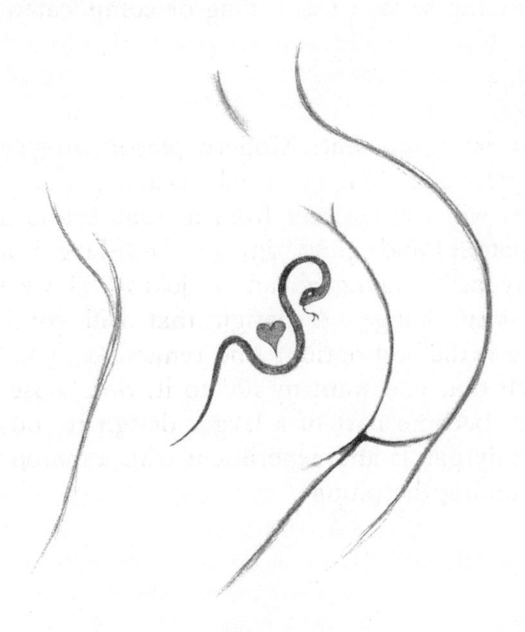

Is it safe?

As with body piercing, you should only be treated by a licensed person who uses sterile and purpose-made equipment. Needles should come wrapped and guaranteed as sterile, and new ones should be used for each client. A professional and trustworthy practitioner will show you the unopened needle packs before using them on you.

Will it hurt?

This obviously depends on the site, size and complexity of the tattoo. There are some people who *want* it to hurt and who find the stinging sensation part of the experience and even think that the more it hurts, the quicker it will heal. This belief doesn't seem to be confirmed by research done on operation scars where healing seems to be slower if pain is involved. If you do find the tattooing uncomfortable, a surface anaesthetic could be used initially and reapplied if the tattooing session was a long or complicated one.

Warning

Tattoos *are* permanent. Modern plastic surgery and laser techniques can remove small tattoos, but even these methods will leave a scar from a small tattoo or indelible white patches and 'ghost' images from larger ones. Think carefully before gong ahead – jokes will wear thin and names *may* change. A design that will continue to be pleasing is the best option. And remember, you may like it so much that you want to add to it. So choose something that can become part of a larger design if you wish. Buy some body paints and experiment with a temporary design before taking the plunge.

BODY HAIRDRESSING

Hair is very sexy, and the length of your hair and how you wear it can send powerful sexual signals to other people.

Body hair – on the arms, legs, underarms, chest and genitals – is often even more important than head hair. Human beings may have body hair as a form of insulation – a leftover from our animal ancestry. These patches of hair also act as traps for pheremones, the chemical messages in sweat that attract the opposite sex. They are particularly rich in the sweat under the arms and around the genitals. In some cultures, women's underarm hair and hair on the legs, far from being thought unfeminine, is seen as raunchy and sexy. In others, pubic hair is removed as a way of focusing attention on the genitals.

Why not experiment with your hairstyle by asking your partner what they like or dislike? You may find that a style to which your partner at first *objects* might actually turn them on most. Since hairstyles *do* send out such powerful signals, we often shy away from asking our partners to have their hair done in such a way because we fear it might attract others.

See if you and your partner might welcome a change in the way you manage your body hair. Might you enjoy it if he shaved his chest and around his genitals? Would you like it if she left her underarm hair to grow, or clipped or shaved her pubic hair?

You could go halfway at first. Using nail scissors, gently clip your pubic hair short and see if you like the effect. Or try shaving the top of the pubic hair to produce a heart shape. If you do decide on shaving, use a sharp razor and plenty of soap, and go slowly and gently. The best technique is to clip the hair short first, and then shave the remaining stubble. You could use depilatory cream (do a patch-test first on nearby skin to make sure you don't have a reaction to this) for outer areas, but do not allow it to come into contact with the internal mucous membranes. Be especially careful when shaving the scrotum. Because it is so wrinkled, it is difficult to shave without nicking. Four hands are better than two!

PAMPERING IT

Having painted and primped, what about lavishing some tender loving care upon your own or your partner's body? Probably the sexiest, most loving thing you can do for a lover is to offer them a massage.

MASSAGE

Westerners, especially the reserved British variety, tend to regard any form of touching with suspicion or alarm. This is a pity since most major civilisations, from China through Japan, India, Persia, Egypt, Greece and Rome, have recognised the simple, animal truth that touch is healing – and very pleasant and sexy, too.

How do you do it?

Get a washable sheet or towel that you won't object to becoming stained. Lay it on your bed, or any other surface you fancy, from the floor in front of the fire to the kitchen table. Warm your hands in a basin of warm water, pour a good dollop of cream or oil on them and rub your palms together. Keep the bottle or tube to hand and start rubbing the warmed oil or cream on your partner. Begin with the innocent spots – back or tummy – down the arms and legs and to the fingers and toes. You may find, incidentally, that these parts are not so innocent after all. Move inwards to the chest or breast and the nipples; then the thighs and the area around the genitals and the genitals themselves. Change places and become the one to be massaged. Then join in together so that both of you are smoothing slippery stuff over each other, using your bodies as well as your hands to slip and slide and rub it well in. And if you are using a flavoured cream or oil, you can sniff and lick and suck it off too.

Best of all, you don't have to buy anything special. Steal the baby's oil, use your last holiday's sun cream or find a more exciting use than frying chips for cooking oil. And if you fancy giving your tastebuds a treat, what's in the kitchen cupboards or the fridge? Honey, jam, peanut butter, or cream? And if you end up sticky, you can always wash it all off each other in the bath or shower.

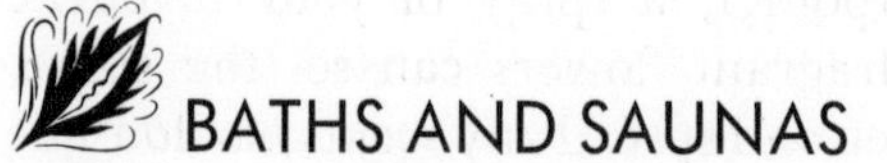

BATHS AND SAUNAS

Having a bath together is more than just a way of saving water. Heat makes you relaxed and aware of your body and its pleasures, and of your partner's body, too. Taking a bath or a sauna together is one of the best possible preludes to love.

If you share a bathroom in a cold, draughty flat, you might find it difficult to create exactly the right atmosphere. But it *can* be done. And don't worry if you don't have access to a private sauna. Your local leisure centre or health club will, quite rightly, object if you try out the following suggestions on their premises, so you might have to have a sauna and then go home to carry out the rest of the plan in private. For a really sexy bath you need:

- atmospheric lighting
- sweet smells
- oils and unguents
- sultry sounds
- luscious nibbles

- scrubbers and flannels
- warm towels

Lighting

Bathroom lights tend to be bleak and harsh. Since water and electricity are a deadly combination, you can't play around with the lights overhead, and certainly shouldn't bring in softer lamps on long flexes. If your overhead light has a bulb, switch it off and *before* running the bath, change it for a softer, coloured bulb that suits your decor – or your complexion. Or fill available *safe* surfaces with candles.

Sweet smells

Incense, a bowl of potpourri, a spray of your favourite perfume or a vase of fragrant flowers can set the scene. Warm steam will heighten and spread any scents, so don't be too heavy-handed. For an especially extravagant whiff, pour some perfumed oil in the loo cistern and every time the loo is flushed it will waft pleasant smells through the room. And, of course, you can pour bath oil or salts into your bath.

Oils and unguents

As well as delighting the nose, what you put in your bath can delight the skin. If your purse cannot run to expensive bath oils, you can use ordinary vegetable oil from the kitchen. A tablespoon in the bath will leave your skin feeling smooth, though it does leave a horrible, oily ring round the bath. You can make up your own bath oil by mixing a tablespoon of vegetable or nut oil with six to ten drops of an essential oil. You could also get some castor or turkey red oil from a healthfood shop. This dissolves in water and will leave less of a ring afterwards.

Women through the ages have bathed in the most extraordinary mixtures, supposedly to improve their complexions and render them irresistible. Nero's wife, Poppaea, and Cleopatra bathed in asses' milk, and Mary Queen of Scots and Anne Boleyn splashed about in wine.

You might want to add herbs and spices to your bath, but do consider the difficulties of scraping off all the bits afterwards. Wrap your herbs in a handkerchief or any square of thin material (muslin is best) and hang under the tap as it fills the bath. Or you could make an infusion of the herbs by pouring boiling water over them in a jug, leaving the mixture to stand for 15 – 20 minutes, then straining it into the bath. Or simply throw in a couple of suitable herbal teabags. Another trick is to add oatmeal to the herbs (two parts to one) to soften the water.

Some herbs are supposed to be stimulating – basil, bay leaf, lavender, lemon verbena, lovage, meadowsweet, rosemary, sage and thyme. Others are said to be relaxing – catnip, chamomile, jasmine, lime flower, vervain. Use rose petals, borage, linden blossom and anything else you like. You can make your own bath salts by mixing a few drops of essential oil to 5 oz (150 g) bicarbonate of soda and 3 oz (75 g) powdered orris root. Mix thoroughly and keep in an air-tight jar – then add a handful to your bath. Don't pour undiluted essential oils straight into a bath. They are strong, and if you use too much, they could give you headaches or irritate the skin.

Some herbs are best when heated, and the most effective way to do this is to take them into the sauna with you. Check with the other patrons first if you are using a public one. If they agree, take in a bunch of chamomile, sage, thyme, verbena or eucalyptus, or some elder or lime flowers. All these will smell wonderful in the hot atmosphere.

Sultry sounds

You may prefer to bathe with just the sound of gently lapping water or your own or your partner's attempts at grand opera. But if music is the food of love . . . how about turning on the stereo? You can get tapes or records of birdsong, waterfalls, the seashore, storms or any other effects you want. Or you might prefer your favourite rock tape, easy listening, jazz, classical – it's up to you. Make sure, however, that what you have chosen is going to last as long as you want. Do not, however, take mains-operated stero equipment into the bathroom, and never operate it when you are wet.

Luscious nibbles

When Anne Boleyn took her baths in white wine, fawning courtiers were said to have dipped their glasses in and toasted her with ribald jokes. You might find it slightly more appealing to take a tray of nibbles and sips with you and to leave the bathwater alone. Forget the full meal – trying to balance a plate of chicken curry on your waterlogged lap is only asking for trouble.

What you should be aiming for is a snack you can feed each other with your fingers, and one that won't ruin the effect if dropped into the water. You want small, stylish, *luxury* foods. Snippets of smoked salmon, perhaps, crunchy salad of mangetouts and baby corn with a dip, quails' eggs or parma ham and melon slices. Try mangoes (the best way to eat them *is* in a bath), slices of avocado or prawns in their shells. But let's face it, even fish and chips can be fun if that's what you like. To drink, try a crystal glass of champagne – or a can of lager if that's more your style. And in winter, why not try mulled wine? You can pour a little in the bath, too.

Scrubbers and flannels

Once you've used a brush or a loofah, you'll realise why they are essential items in any sensual bathroom. Scrubbed skin tingles and glows. As well as feeling clean, it feels alive and sensitive. Soft sponges and soaped flannels can then be used to soothe and smooth. If you really want to scrub any dirt away, mix a handful of coarse kitchen salt with an equal amount of vegetable oil and a couple of drops of essential oil. Rub yourself, or each other, vigorously all over, being careful of the delicate areas, and then rinse off before having a warm (not hot) bath or shower.

Towels

After your bath, wrap each other in warm towels. You might like to dry yourself briskly, or to relax in comfort and gently drip dry. If your bathroom floor is cold, put some extra towels down for comfort. And try to make sure that all towels *are* warm – wrap them round a hot water bottle while you bathe if you don't have a heated rail.

Hot and cold

The contrast of hot and cold can be surprisingly arousing. Warmth will loosen and relax your muscles. And cold can get your circulation going, making your skin tingle excitingly. A combination may be best of all.

You can heat yourself up with a hot bath or shower, or a sauna if you have one. Then splash yourself quickly with cold water or with a cold blast from the shower. While the skin is still tingling from the cold, snuggle up to your partner and let the inner heat catch up with you both. Or you can put a bowl of hand-hot water, a flannel and a bowl of ice cubes next to your bed, or wherever else you are planning to make love. Use them turn and turn about to give some interesting contrasts. Crunch an ice cube in your mouth and then have oral sex using your cold tongue and lips on your partner's genitals. For a greater contrast, hold the warm flannel to their genitals first. Or reverse things by swilling a mouthful of hot water, or any other liquid, and (if you can bear it,) pop an ice cube into/on to an intimate spot, and then get it together. Experiment with flannel and ice cube on nipples, toes, earlobes and whatever else takes your fancy.

Warning

Don't use ice cubes straight from the freezer as they can stick to your skin and give a nasty case of freezer burn. Use only a small and already melting piece of ice at first and for intimate places. And test any hot water you use to make sure it won't scald, remembering that delicate areas, such as the penis and vagina, are far more sensitive than hardened fingertips.

USING IT

Where and how you make love can make an enormous difference to your excitement and pleasure.

PLACES

Many of us tend to feel that once we're married or living together, lovemaking should only take place in the bedroom. Hot and heavy gropings on living room sofas, in cinemas, on the beach or behind the bike sheds are not seen as dignified behaviour for established couples. This is a pity because routine and predictability may give you security, but they can also be the death of sexy and exciting lovemaking. Without giving offence to anyone else, you might like to think about how you could be more adventurous in where you make love.

Why not use the rest of the house? Make sure no one is going to barge in (put the cat out and lock your doors) and snuggle up on the sofa or the living room floor. If you have a sturdy kitchen table, hop up on that and pull your partner into an irresistible clinch. Offer to scrub your partner's back next time they have a bath or shower and don't waste time drying off and moving to the bedroom. Half the fun can be the discomfort and the ridiculousness of making love in the 'wrong' places. Some places can also help with sexual positions – if you want to try making love standing up, having the shorter partner one step up on the stairs may be useful. There can also be the added edge of the fear of being caught.

While enjoying the risk, don't indulge yourselves at the expense of other people. It's rude to confront other adults with your sexual activities, and possibly traumatically upsetting to younger people. Don't take needless risks if there are children about.

With those warnings in mind, you can go farther afield. Perhaps the ultimate in risky exhibitionist behaviour is the so-called 'Mile-High Club'. This is not a club as such, but you become a 'member' if you make love in a plane. Don't forget the captain has the right to land at the nearest airport and eject you if your behaviour is upsetting other passengers. And the airline has the right to bill you for the cost of such a detour – it can run into thousands of pounds. So coupling in the aisle or locking yourself in the tiny loo could prove expensive.

Alfresco or open-air sex can be delicious. Find yourself a quiet hillside or forest glade or a private corner of a field.

Warning

When making love outdoors, beware of insects or plants that bite or sting, and watch out for sunburn on places that aren't usually exposed. You should also bear in mind that farm animals, especially cattle, can be very curious. You may recover from a bout of passion to find a milk herd standing around you making critical comments and blowing chewed grass all over you. And the farmer might stroll across to see what is bothering his cows . . .

People have made love in lifts, ski gondolas, art galleries, restaurants, theatre boxes and trains – you name it and someone has tried it. If your behaviour is *not* offensive to anyone else – that is, it remains private even though it is in a public place – you are harming no one. If you *are* seen, however, you could be had up for a range of offences, so do make sure the risk of discovery that may spur you on remains *only* a risk. As long as the behaviour does not become compulsive or obsessive – that is, you are always in control and choose to do it and don't find that you need to be at risk to become excited – you aren't harming yourself either.

One tip: even if you have no other reason to use them, condoms are a great help in alfresco sex if you want to avoid the embarrassment of damp patches.

SEXUAL GYMNASTICS

You can vary how you make love as well as where. It is a sad fact that only one position for lovemaking seems to be accepted as the correct way of doing it – the 'missionary' position where the man lies on top and in between the legs of his partner, supporting himself on his elbows. The problem with this position is that it can be quite limiting for both partners. If the man is not to lean heavily on the woman, he has to keep both hands or elbows down, which makes it difficult to caress her breasts or her clitoris or other parts. His penis can receive all the stimulation it needs from the in-and-out motion he can control, but his partner may find the speed, thrust and angle of penetration simply does not excite or satisfy her. Sadly, some women gain very little from the experience – except the ability to fake it. In contrast, there are a host of postions that *could* add new and extraordinary dimensions to your lovemaking.

In the *T'ung Hsuan Tzu*, written in the seventeenth century, the Chinese physician Li T'ung Hsuan describes four basic lovemaking postions and 26 main variations. He gives the variations delightful names such as 'two fishes side by side', 'flying butterflies', 'cat and mice share a hole', 'leaping wild horses', 'mandarin ducks intertwined' and 'a phoenix plays in a red cave'. His names for the four basic positions are equally poetic: 'close union' for man on top of woman, 'unicorn horn' for woman on man, 'intimate attachment' for side by side, 'sunning fish' for man entering from the rear.

Woman on top

In this position, the woman lies on her partner with both legs astride his, or one or both inside his thighs. He may be able to take her weight on his chest, allowing her to have one or both hands free to caress him or guide his hands. She can decide the angle and the pace of movement and may well find that she climaxes far more easily in this position. He can have his hands entirely free to stroke and hold her, to touch her breasts or clitoris. Men often find this position, being less tiring, allows them to last longer and to enjoy lovemaking more.

Side by side

Both lovers lie face to face on their sides. It can be difficult to enter in this position, and you might like to start off with one or the other on top and then roll over. You also need to hold on and move together or you might lose touch. It makes for long, slow, gentle and loving sex with both of you able to touch and hold to your hearts' content.

Standing up

This is especially good for in-the-shower fun or while using the washing machine as an extra vibrator. If the woman is much shorter than the man, you might need a footstool, or she could wrap her legs round his thighs, while he holds her up by the bottom or thighs.

Sitting down

He sits in a chair, on a bench or on the edge of the bed and she sits in his lap facing him with her legs astride his. This position, like woman on top, gives her control and him staying power, and allows him to use his tongue or lips on her breasts.

From the rear

You can do it 'doggie fashion' with the woman lying on her stomach or kneeling over a chair, bed or pillow. Or he can sit in a chair or lean back against pillows and she can sit in his lap with her back to him. Many people find this is a particularly exciting position, and others find it slightly shocking, simply because it reminds them of the way animals have sex. Many men find it an extremely arousing position, and it does allow either or both partners to touch the woman's clitoris to make sure she is satisfied, too.

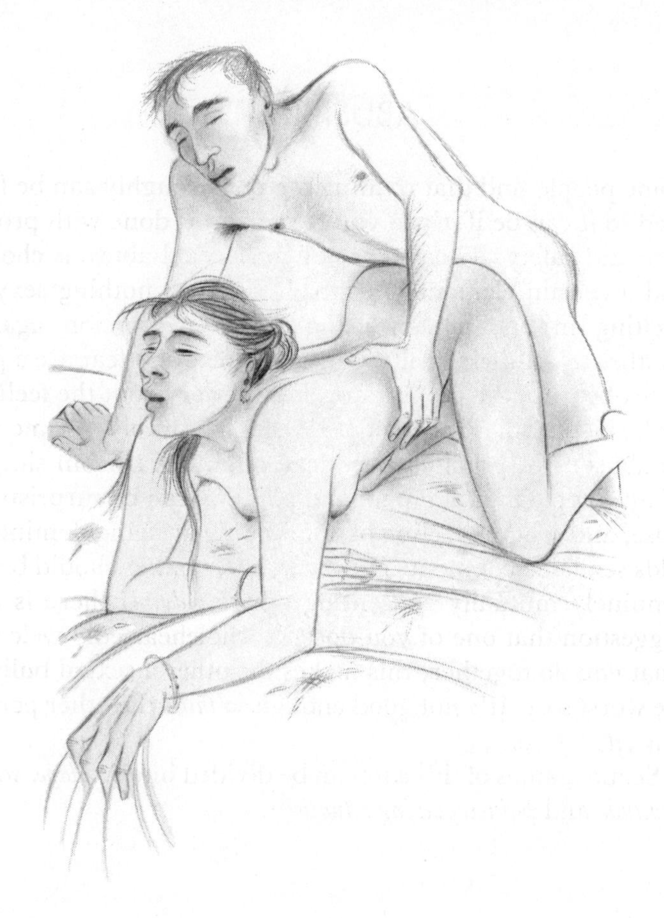

Of course these are only the *basic* positions. You can ring all sorts of changes by shifting legs, bending or straightening knees, sitting up, leaning over, or using pillows, blankets, chairs or tables to support you. But the main point of all this is *not* to say that lovemaking swinging from a chandelier or standing up in a hammock is automatically any better or any more exciting than straight man or woman sex. What *is* true, however, is that trying something different *if you both want to*, might prove pleasant. You don't have to tie yourself in knots, but neither do you have to lie still and do it only one way. Experiment a little and see what tickles your fancy.

ABUSING IT

Some people find that treating the body roughly can be fun. And so it can be if it's to your taste and is done with proper care and safety. The essence of consensual abuse is choice, and a certain element of control. There is nothing sexy or exciting in one person using force or coercion against another to get their thrills. When violence and fear are a part of sex because the perpetrator doesn't *care* about the feelings of the victim, that isn't sex or love – it's simply a crime and an abuse. But private desires can often be far from simple. Many people find that pain and pleasure can be surprisingly close, and that the feeling of dominating or being dominated adds sexual excitement. However, such games should be for genuinely mutually consenting adults *only*. If there is any suggestion that one of you doesn't wholeheartedly welcome what you do together, this makes the other a sexual bully of the worst sort. It's not good enough to *think* the other person consents – ASK.

Sexual games of this sort can be divided into *bondage, sexual servitude* and *pain-involving situations*.

BONDAGE

You can use restraints in various forms for sexual pleasure. The simplest bondage may involve using a tie, belt or scarf to secure one of you to the bed while the other plays out a domination or rape fantasy. But you can also buy handcuffs or custom-made restraints, equipment and clothing to extend your fantasy. There are chains and padlocks, padded leather wrist- and ankle-cuffs and collars. You can have harnesses made of metal, rope and leather that tie hands behind the back or to the waist, thighs, ankles or neck. There are blindfolds and gags, and 'spreader bars' that fasten to wrists, thighs or ankles to force them apart and stop you bringing them together.

How do you use it?

Agree *beforehand* how far you wish to go and what you want to do. It would be wise to have an agreed word or phrase that you can use to stop the action immediately and without argument.

Bondage equipment can include ropes, chains and harnesses to fasten your partner to the bed, the floor or the ceiling. Make sure the fabric is strong enough to take this and won't suddenly come apart in a passion-killing shower of plaster or splintering wood. If you take your drills and screws away on holiday or when visiting friends, it is considered 'good form' to fill in the holes and leave everything as you found it.

Warning

Bondage can be fun, but it can also be very dangerous if care isn't taken. Some of the headgear and gags could be particularly risky if used unwisely. Never ever tie anything so tight that it blocks breathing or can't be released quickly. It is the sense of danger that gives bondage its spice for some people, but you must think and plan carefully before you use it.

SEXUAL SERVITUDE

Bondage equipment and clothing can also be used as part of sexual servitude games, where one partner allows the other to assume total domination.

How do you use them?

As well as cuffs and shackles, you can buy complete harnesses of straps, D-rings and buckles. Some are 'chastity' barriers, to prevent the wearer having sex. Those for women may have leather plates covering the genitals, attached to a belt or neck collar with buckles that can be closed with a padlock. Those for men may involve a leather sheath tied with thongs and attached to a leash. Some harnesses are exactly the opposite in that they display and even support breasts or genitals and everything is on show. If you have pierced nipples or genitals, you can also buy harnesses and straps that incorporate rings to go through the pierced holes.

Master and slave games may involve bondage, or they may not. The idea, however, is for the slave to do exactly what she – or more usually he – is told. This can involve cleaning the kitchen floor while wearing only a leather harness or a posing pouch, then preparing a meal and serving it without eating himself. If he's been a good slave, he may be rewarded with sex.

A close relation to this is the 'grown-up baby' game. This often seems to be favoured by high-powered and highly stressed male executives who want to give up all responsibility and decision-making as their form of relaxation. Played to the full, it involves dressing in giant nappies, lying in cots and being fed, from bottle or breast, by their 'mother'.

PAIN INVOLVING SITUATIONS

Bondage or sexual servitude may also involve sadomasochism (or SM) – the giving or receiving of pain for sexual arousal. Slapping the skin causes blood to rush to the abused area, irritating and heating it. The resulting engorgement can mimic or heighten sensations of pleasure as sexual arousal also causes tissue to flush and engorge.

How do you use it?

You can play spanking games – a few slaps on the bottom with your hand – but some people go further and buy tawses, canes, cat o'nine tails or whips to do the beating. Some sex toy firms advertise a smacked botty cream to soothe the smarting skin, but baby lotion is cheaper and does the job just as well.

Warning

Dressing up, tying up or hitting out are often thought of as perverted activities, but they are actually more common than many would admit. Most of the time, they are essentially harmless and private indulgences, *if*, that is, you keep your behaviour to yourself or share it only with a willing and happy companion. But it must be said that *any* activity becomes worrying when, instead of adding to your love life, it dominates it. If you find you get excited and are satisfied when clothing and games are used, on occasion, that is fine. But if you find you cannot be aroused or interested *unless* they are used, or that the object or the game rather than your partner is what arouses you, then you may need counselling (see the addresses on pages 171 – 2).

5
THINGS FANTASTICAL

Sex, says one notable expert, is a matter of friction and fantasy – 90 per cent fantasy to 10 per cent friction! Having sexual fantasies is not just common, it's virtually universal. Our fantasies may be thoughts and wishes that just pop into our minds and play themselves out without any conscious control. Or they may be the result of deliberate daydreaming, and proceed exactly as we wish them to. Fantasies may only touch on sexual themes. You might indulge in a little gentle wish fulfilment, dreaming about someone you fancy giving you a compliment. You may day-dream as a relief from everyday life, and imagine yourself in a luxurious, exotic location. Or, fantasies may be specifically sexual and be dream scenarios of sexual encounters, maybe extending to 'unusual' sexual practices such as sadomasochism, bestiality or group sex.

WHO FANTASISES?

The answer is *most* people, though there's nothing wrong with you if you don't. But as it is more likely that you *have* had fantasies, there's no reason to feel guilty or afraid. It certainly doesn't mean you are unusual or abnormal, or that something must be missing from your sexual relationship. As many as 71 per cent of men and 72 per cent of women in some studies say they have fantasised to increase their excitement while having sex with a partner. And, according to another study, women who rate both themselves and their partners as good lovers are *more* likely to use sexual fantasy than those who think of themselves or their partners as being poor in bed.

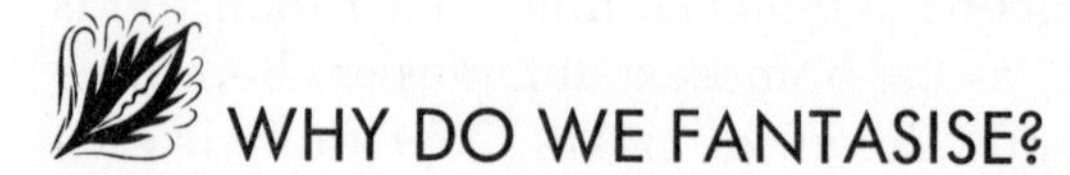

WHY DO WE FANTASISE?

We can use fantasy as a substitute for the real thing. Almost all men say they fantasise when they masturbate, for instance, and masturbation without it would probably be rather unsatisfying. But it seems that fantasy is mainly used as an 'extra', while actually making love.

Fantasy can also give relief from the tensions and worries you might have about your sexual behaviour. In your own mind and under your control, no sexual partner is going to laugh at your body, disparage your technique or question your tastes. Fantasy provides a totally safe environment to try things out. If you haven't had oral sex, or haven't made it in the bath or tried it in the open air . . . you can rehearse the scene in the knowledge that nothing will go wrong. Fantasy also allows you to run through activities in your mind that might give you a thrill in theory, but which you would actually hate experiencing in reality – rape, for instance.

The great advantage of fantasy is that you are in total control. In effect, the fantasy is a film and you are the producer, director, scriptwriter, casting agency and camera operator. Every scene begins, proceeds and ends exactly as you want it to. In these dreams, we can forget about all the guilts, anxieties and embarrassments of real life and get on with what we *want* to do.

WHAT DO PEOPLE FANTASISE ABOUT?

There are as many fantasies as there are people, but particular elements seem to crop up in most people's thoughts. Top of the list is making love to someone other than your actual partner – a celebrity, perhaps, or a former lover (usually remembered through rose-tinted glasses!) or a friend, neighbour, colleague or a stranger seen in passing. Making love to someone younger or much older than you is also quite common, as are homosexual fantasies. Both men and women frequently dream of making love to their own partners, but in an exotic place such as a beach, jungle or mountainside, or on a bearskin rug in front of a blazing fire or in a mirror-lined room.

Another common fantasy is of being watched while making love or of watching others do so – human or animal. Clothing can figure in these fantasies. Suspenders and stockings, high heels, uniforms or leather and rubber are the most common items. Both men and women indulge in rape fantasies, picturing themselves as the victim or the aggressor. And harems, sheikhs, master/slave, group sex and bondage are regularly reported as fantasy favourites.

HOW CAN YOU USE YOUR FANTASIES?

Fantasies can make simple masturbation into elaborate and stunning loveplay. But many people also use fantasy to enliven their joint love. It can get you aroused, it can prolong excitement during lovemaking, and can bring on orgasm and make the afterglow even brighter.

No one can tell what you're thinking, which means you can indulge in anything at all without it harming or embarrassing you. You can use fantasy as a rehearsal, and can run through any variation or new experience you like and consider whether or not you might like to try it for real.

Why don't you . . . ?

Think about a sexual variation you've heard or read about – something you are curious about and might want to consider, but have never tried. Something you've seen in this book – perhaps using a vibrator on yourself or your partner or dressing up in unusual clothing. Choose a time when you won't get disturbed. It might not be a good idea to indulge while driving home during the rush hour, or chopping vegetables! Picture yourself doing it and see how you feel. Excited? Run through it a few times and add or subtract details until you've got it right.

You can also use 'rehearsal' fantasy to consider something you know your partner might like, but that until now you haven't been too keen on trying. For instance, both men and women often say they wish their partner would try oral sex. You can imagine yourself doing this, and run through the elements that put you off and those that seem OK. Use your fantasy to see whether you could find a way of playing down the parts you don't like.

You can also use fantasy as an escape. This might be useful if there are parts of your relationship you aren't happy about but don't yet feel ready to try and change. If you aren't entirely satisfied, you can at least play things out the way you want them in your mind. And you can use fantasy as a way of having experiences you would never actually want to play for real – other partners or different sexual activities. Thinking about being unfaithful isn't the same as doing it, and nobody gets hurt or betrayed by a fantasy.

Once you've allowed yourself to have fantasies and have explored and enjoyed them, you might like to consider sharing them with your partner. Talking about your fantasies with your partner *can* be risky, so go carefully. Some people find it difficult to accept that their partner fantasises, even though they do it themselves. They may feel insulted, as if by having fantasies you are saying that their lovemaking isn't good enough. Or they may be afraid of having to compete with your dreams. Or they may simply be embarrassed.

You could begin by talking about other people's fantasies. The author Nancy Friday has produced several books (see Further Reading, page 175–6) on male and female sexual fantasy, and these could make for interesting night-time reading. Take turns to pick out and read a fantasy that interests, disgusts or arouses you, and tell your partner why it makes you feel this way.

You may be perfectly happy keeping your fantasies to yourself and not sharing them. Fantasies are very private and it certainly doesn't mean that you distrust or don't love your partner if you want to keep quiet. Like so many aspects of love and relationships, that's simply a matter of taste. But if you both want to share each other's fantasy lives, you could suggest to your partner that you try out whatever it was you 'rehearsed'. You don't have to tell them you have prepared yourself by fantasising, but doing so might break the ice: 'Guess what I was thinking about last night? I know you've always wanted to try . . . Well, I think I might like to give it a go.'

If you aren't yet 100 per cent sure about revealing your fantasies, you could start by keeping each other guessing. Talk about fantasies you have heard and read about . . . and slip in one that *is* your own. If you feel able and relaxed enough, tell your partner which one is yours. If you are happy so far, go one stage further . . .

Make a contract that you will each describe a fantasy and listen to the other say if it excites them or does nothing for them. Agree that you *won't* laugh at your partner, or criticise them, for having that particular fantasy.

Then you might like to make up a fantasy and describe it to your partner. You can do this while making supper, in bed with the lights off, having a bath together, or you could phone them at work during a lunch or tea break, or think up your own time and place to do it.

Why don't you . . . tell a story?

While you are together, alone and relaxed, start describing a fantasy. You can stay fully dressed, just sitting together, or you may find as your description unfolds that you both want to kiss and caress and then make love. Agree beforehand whether one of you will tell the whole story, whether you will take it in turns to advance the action or whether one of you will take over halfway. You are more than likely to find that what turns you on is very different. But it's also likely that you can combine elements that excite both of you and that you can conjure up a scenario together that satisfies you equally. If you are comfortable with this and want to go further . . .

Why don't you . . . write a script?

So far, all the action has taken place in your mind. Now you might like to progress and act out a favourite fantasy. Maybe you imagine you're a slave in an Eastern palace, or an attractive stranger being picked up by an equally good-looking one in a bar, or you're being taken by storm by a delivery man or woman while your partner is out. Write the script of what you would like to happen. It could be just an outline, with a brief idea of what you each say, or exact speeches (don't expect your partner to remember their lines word for word – the basic drift is enough). Agree a time to try it out. You could act out your scene at home, or even meet up in a pub or restaurant to make it seem more real. You may collapse in giggles or be tongue-tied with embarrassment. That doesn't matter, just go on trying. It sometimes works perfectly first time, and you may be amazed at how much it adds to your love life.

If you are happy about role-playing, you might like to use props to enhance your fantasy play-acting. If so . . .

Why don't you . . . go the whole way?

Think about your fantasies and what sort of extras might really bring them alive. Would clothing help? A French maid outfit or a leather harness, or a latex raincoat and boots? Would equipment help? A whip, or straps or ribbons to tie you down? Talk it over, and if you agree, polish up your script, order your goods and set your date.

A warning here if you are thinking of using music in your chosen scenario. Music is all about rhythm and tempo, and unless your physical exertions match it exactly, the results can be comical or disastrous. Music is probably best kept as a prelude, not an accompaniment, to sex. However, there are other recorded sounds available, and if you and your partner have a shared passion for, say, grand prix racing or steam trains or birdsong, you can now buy tapes or discs of sound effects to enhance your sexual pleasure.

A final word on fantasies

Almost everyone is a fantasy figure to *someone*, and it can be an ego boost in itself to fantasise about who might be fantasising over *you*. Fantasy can also be a great leveller if you have any doubts about your own attractiveness or social status. Have you ever wondered, for example, who the partners of the accepted fantasy figures, like film and pop stars, dream about? It's quite reassuring to think that a Mrs Harrison Ford might spend her time fantasising about the mail man!

Fantasy is normal, common and harmless, up to a point. But there are exceptions, and if you find yourself constantly resorting to daydreams maybe you should ask yourself if there are problems in your life or in your relationship that you are trying to avoid or escape. If so, it would be worth seeking help to solve these problems, rather than getting deeper and deeper into unreality. If fantasy is not just an extra bit of spice in your love life, but so essential you couldn't have successful sex without it, then you should definitely look for help. Maybe you need some counselling (see pages 171 – 2) . . . or a new partner?

6

THINGS VISUAL

Sex is supposed to be private, but most of us can be interested or aroused by the thought, sight or sound of other people's bodies and other people's lovemaking. We may like something that can stimulate or set off our private fantasies; we may want a hint or a reminder to get ourselves or a partner going; or we may want specific ideas for positions, additions or variations. Whatever, there is now wealth of material available, in the form of videos, films, cassette tapes, magazines and books.

All of these may be made specifically for the purpose of rousing sexual feeling. Or you can find material that has an artistic intention but just happens to contain images or ideas (or people) that turn you on.

Many people believe that pornographic material corrupts and degrades and that viewing it will lead to sexual abuse. These fears are often fuelled by rape and child sexual abuse cases when the men involved claim that reading or seeing pornography 'drove' them to it. The evidence is far from clear, however.

Sexually explicit material is seen by millions of people who do *not* rape or abuse. Many cultures make such material a part of their love lives, and always have. The Japanese, for instance, have an astoundingly low incidence of rape, yet violently explicit popular comics are available at every bookstall. So surely the impact of pornography has to do with *what* it shows, and *how* and *why* you use it. I would suggest that any material that arouses sexual feelings, but does so in the context of respect for your partner or others, is acceptable. Whereas material which encourages you to think of other people as objects for your use is immoral, damaging and dangerous.

There is a belief that women are the opposite of men in that they are more aroused by words than by pictures. In the 1950s, Kinsey found that five times as many women responded to written material as to pictures or films. It was also suggested that women are aroused more by suggestion than by explicit sex. However, there are no real psychological or physical reasons for such a difference, except that when a man is excited it is obvious. Arousal in a woman can be concealed from onlookers and even ignored by the woman herself.

Recent studies carried out by women researchers indicate that women can be just as turned on by pornography as their male partners, providing they find the material is attractive. Unfortunately, the vast majority of current pornography shows sex only as some men want it. Women are presented, not as people with whom one shares lovemaking, but as objects with which a man can achieve excitement and orgasm.

What we really need is a move away from pornography and towards erotica. Pornography is usually about the sexual act alone, or simply about bits of the body. Women are shown either being abused or just as 'tits and bums' for men's titillation. It is not surprising that most women, and quite a few men, find this a turn-off. What both sexes might prefer is erotica, which is to do with sex and sensuality, pleasure and mutual respect.

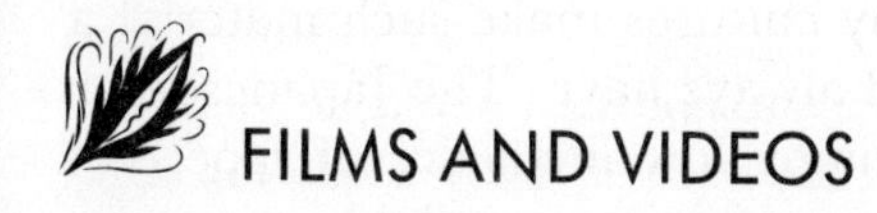

FILMS AND VIDEOS

Video shops, sex shops, mail-order firms and some specialist cinemas offer films that are supposed to excite and arouse you. The storyline usually contains standard elements: an innocent young girl leaves a convent and embarks on a journey of sexual discovery; an innocent young girl is led astray into a world of drugs and depravity; an innocent young boy is initiated into sex by lustful older women, etc, etc. The locations often appear to be exotic and luxurious, the sex is frequent and the actors attractive.

There are plenty of bare breasts, bottoms and pubic mounds, but no erect penises and very few glimpses of even flaccid ones. Sexual acts are simulated explicitly, but they are *only* simulated. The overall quality of the films may be poor, the acting unconvincing, the clothes very out of date and the soundtrack dubbed and out of synch with lip movements. Don't be misled by the covers on the boxes. These are often far more suggestive than the video itself and often have nothing to do with the actual content. Depending on your mood, you may howl with laughter, or find one of these videos can get you in the mood for sex. There are also plenty of films on general release that are not specifically intended to be used for sexual purposes, but can be very sexy. Films that feature your favourite stars usually have at least one love scene and these are actually often far more arousing than the action in the purpose-made videos.

Why not 'go to the pictures' at home? Tell your partner you are planning a video evening and make sure you will be alone and undisturbed. Wear something sexy that you can strip off easily, dim the lights, pour your favourite drink and start the film. Snuggle close and when a sexy scene that excites you comes on, say 'I wouldn't mind doing that with you.' You can always rewind the film to the point at which other things claimed your interest!

Of course, you could also go to the cinema to watch a film that turns you on. But have the courtesy to sit at the back, and not to disturb other patrons, or save your passion until you get home.

Hard-core pornographic films showing explicit sexual acts and genitals are not legally available in this country. Sending such material through the post is also illegal, so bear in mind that mail-order films offering to sell such material could be leading you on, since they would be prosecuted if caught doing so. Hard-core pornography is often very brutal and particularly prone to showing women as bits of bodies rather than people. In my view pornography that shows rape and other violence, or the abuse of animals and children, has no place in an acceptable relationship or a civilised society.

SOUND TAPES

Jane Birkin scandalised some and delighted others in the 1960s with her record 'Je t'aime', which featured thinly disguised lovemaking, with sighs and eventual simulated orgasm. Today you can ring phonelines or buy tapes and listen to men or women making suggestive remarks or relating their supposed sexual adventures. As with films, 'erotic' sound tapes can be so stagey and obvious that they produce amusement rather than arousal. But again, some of them get you going if you are in the right mood. You might find some music recordings with openly sexual lyrics and driving, rhythmic beats or soft romantic sounds even more exciting.

MAGAZINES

What most people don't realise is that the pictures you see in magazines and newspapers are the result of a lot of behind-the-scenes work. Transparent tape is used to lift and support those apparently firm and gravity-defying breasts. Stretchmarks and other blemishes are covered with make-up or painted out of the finished picture. Ice cubes, blasts of air or a quick tweak and flick make nipples stand out. The average woman's body could look just as smooth and taut if given the same treatment. But a 'normal' body is just as beautiful with its soft breasts, lines and bulges, if we could only accept that this *is* the real thing.

If the only bodies you see are these unrealistic paper images, you might be critical of your own, or your partner's, apparently flawed body. For this reason, 'blue' magazines can be distressing to women, even though they often excite their men. Of course, there are versions of such magazines for women, and an American magazine is available from some newsagents in this country that shows pin-ups of athletes and male models. There are also magazines of men posing which are intended for other men – but do just as well for women. So, if you find the fact that your partner looks at nude photos distressing, why not get some for yourself and see if they turn you on.

There are magazines with explicit artwork and articles that cater for particular sexual interests such as body art, and leather and rubber clothing. And there are other magazines that can be highly erotic although they are not specifically produced with sexual arousal in mind. These can be sporting magazines – surfing, skiing, climbing, body-building, aerobics and keep-fit – that have pictures of both sexes in attractive poses and revealing sports clothing. The bodies are in superb condition and frequently beautiful, and these magazines can be very sexy if you like that sort of thing.

BOOKS

Books have been a form of sex aid since our ancestors first started making something a bit more portable than a painting on a cave wall. The Chinese had 'Pillow Books', that contained text and pictures of lovemaking that lovers could read together and imitate. Far from being considered pornographic, such books were seen as an essential part of the art of love.

There is a wealth of classic erotic literature available, from the Roman Petronius's *Satyricon*, through Chaucer's *Canterbury Tales*, *Tom Jones*, *The Decameron* and *Fanny Hill* to the more recent *Lady Chatterley's Lover* and *The Story of O*. You may find any or all of these arousing, or you may find passages in mainstream novels, pictures in art books or suggestions in books such as this helpful in your lovemaking.

Why not play this game with your partner? By next Saturday night you will both bring magazines or books to bed to show each other. You should each come up with something that gets *you* going and something you think will get *them* going. There are two prizes – one for the item that gets you going best, and another for the item that gets them going. Obviously, you could each win either or both prizes. Whichever way it goes, you could learn something for next time. And the prize? Why not make it first choice of the lovemaking positions, or a massage, or any other sexy treat you both enjoy?

DO IT YOURSELF

There are various ways you can use visual erotica of your own making to spice up your love life. For instance, you can make photographs, tapes or videos of yourself and your partner. Many people find the sight of themselves and their partners 'in flagrante delicto' exciting, and would like to have more opportunities to watch what happens at times when they might otherwise have their eyes closed.

You could use a polaroid camera or a video camera to take candid shots of each other, or both of you together, in poses or in action. Or put the tape recorder on when you make love and records the sounds of your lovemaking. Next time you feel amorous, bring out the tape or the photos and show your partner and see if this gets you aroused.

Since these recordings are made by you and do not need to be processed or developed by anyone else, they are not illegal, as long as they are for your own private use. However, if you send them through the post you could be charged with sending indecent material by mail. And if you take photographs on ordinary film and have them developed you might be in trouble. Most developing and printing is now done automatically, so your films could be printed and handed back without comment. But if they are also checked by a supervisor and that person is offended or shocked, you could be reported to the police. Or barred from ever using *that* camera shop again!

You can also watch yourselves making love by placing mirrors strategically to show the two of you on the bed from various angles. If you don't want visitors to guess what you are up to, put the mirror on the inside of a wardrobe door and leave the door ajar when you go to bed. Or get a mirror on a stand, and just wheel it out of the way when not in use.

If you would like to cover a wider area, mirror tiles can be used to make the whole wall reflective, or try reflective wallpaper. You might be able to buy these from your nearest DIY store or from a photographers' or artists' suppliers. You could also use both the tiles and the paper on the ceiling. A word of warning: as mirrors can be merciless in bright light, you might like to try them out for the first time by the kind and flickering light of candles.

As has already been discussed, there are conflicting views about erotic material and no conclusive evidence one way or the other. What *is* clear is that the sort of material two consenting, mature adults may find a pleasing addition to their love lives could be disturbing to anyone *not* prepared or too young to understand it. You have a responsibility to keep your private lives private and not to leave such material where it might offend or alarm others.

7
Things Personal

Many people believe that all you really need for a good sex life is another person. For some, extra people add extra fun. And for others, solo pleasure is far from lonely. What part can people play in enhancing your love life?

SOLO SEX

Circumstances or choice may find us alone, but still wanting sexual pleasure. Some cultures see self-pleasing or masturbation as a natural and normal part of sexual expression, the first and most obvious way we explore our bodies and learn how they respond to touch. Sadly, some other cultures see masturbation as wasteful or wicked, or perverted and abnormal. This is particularly true of certain religions which insist that sex should only be for the purpose of creating new life.

There are often fears that masturbation will somehow become 'addictive', that once you try it you won't want to experience the 'real thing'. Certainly, if when you make love to someone else you do so in silence, without sharing with them the discoveries you have made in masturbating, sex might come off a poor second in arousing and satisfying you. And if you have experienced good loving at your own hands, you will know enough to be disappointed at clumsy or insensitive handling by someone else. The answer is not to deny yourself the pleasure of masturbation but to learn all you can and pass it on to your partner.

Masturbation is sex with the person who knows you best. It can be a deeply comforting or exciting experience and one that can satisfy you at the time, or teach you for the future. You should never be ashamed or guilty at pleasing yourself. Many people in normal happy relationships masturbate by themselves on occasions. It doesn't mean they love their partner any less or that they are missing anything in their shared love life. Sex can be like food – sometimes you want to grab a quick snack; sometimes you want to linger over a feast; sometimes you want to share a meal; and sometimes you want to treat yourself, by yourself.

Why not treat yourself to a bit of solo loving? Run a bath and lock the bathroom door, or make sure everyone is out and spread yourself over the bed or sofa. Don't hurry – take your time. Fill your hands with soap or cream or oil and slowly stroke yourself all over. Using the flats of the fingers, sweep from your neck, down the arms and rub and knead your hands. Then place both hands on the chest. Gently rub, squeeze and tweak your nipples and then proceed across your stomach and down the thighs to knees, calves, ankles and feet. Massage your toes last.

Then, rub fingers and palms around your genitals, probing gently for whichever areas feel especially good. Women will explore the clitoris, the inner and outer labia and the vagina. Men will feel the scrotum and the perineum (the area behind the scrotum) as well as the shaft and head of the penis. Use gentle scratches, squeezes, palm and finger strokes, light, firm and hard taps. As you come near to orgasm, concentrate on what you need to tip you over. Relax, and enjoy it. Tuck into your memory what you did that was particularly pleasant. If or when you next make love with a partner, show them.

Learning good masturbation techniques can be helpful to everyone. It can help to learn what pleases you so that you can get the best out of loving. And it can help your partner, if you show them how best to please you. It can help people on their own to continue to feel valued and loved in their own right. It can help people at risk of sexual infections by showing them how much enjoyment they can still have from non-penetrative sex. It can help couples for whom intercourse is difficult because of age, illness or physical handicap. In short, self-loving is true loving and is something about which no one should feel bad.

AFFAIRS

People having affairs often argue that it can have a beneficial effect on their emotional and sexual relationship with their partner. Women sometimes report having their first orgasm with a lover after years of unsatisfactory sex with partners, and say that this helps to improve married sex. Some say that an affair gives them confidence and self-esteem and makes them feel sexually exciting and experienced. In one study two out of three *married* men thought an affair would not be important in their marriage, and that they would forgive, or expect to be forgiven one. However, half of *divorced* men thought that fidelity was vital. When an affair does happen and is discovered, infidelity has the power to hurt more deeply than any other act between couples.

The simple fact is that, whatever self-justifying excuses you come up with, an affair is a betrayal. Some people feel that if you don't actually have intercourse with the person you are seeing, or if it is a gay relationship and your main relationship is straight, then it isn't really an affair. I am of the opinion that if a major part of your time or emotional commitment is invested in another person, it's an affair. To have one, you have to lie and cheat, even if a partner never asks awkward questions or notices what is going on. Whether you think the risks are worthwhile is your choice. My view is that, while some couples fully believe their infidelities help their main relationship, this could be a case of self-deception as well as partner-deception. You always walk a knife-edge during and after an affair, and if your main relationship is going through difficulties, it might be better to work them out *with* your partner – or have the honesty to call it a day. This way you would avoid the emotional and physical dangers that can come with *all* extra-marital sexual involvement.

Emotional dangers

You may think you can keep control of the various commitments and involvements, but sharing sexual love with more than one person can be unsettling. You, your partner or your lover might find powerful jealousies interfering with the nature of your entanglement. One of you might find that what began as a light flirtation becomes more serious. If one of you falls in love with the lover and out of love with the partner, someone is going to get hurt. And what of the lover in all this? He or she is also a real person with real feelings – not just a sophisticated sex aid. What if *they* fall in love and want to take the relationship further than a mere affair?

Physical dangers

Bringing one or more extra people into your relationship also brings the risk of sexual infections. It isn't the *nature* of the sexual relationship that does this – you aren't immune from sexual infections within marriage, and prone to them as some sort of divine punishment outside it. But the more people you share sexually, the more chance you have of exchanging body fluids with someone who is carrying a nasty bug. HIV – the virus that can cause AIDS – can be present for up to ten years before causing symptoms. And while anal sex and sharing needles or injecting drugs are particularly efficient means of passing on the virus, *anyone* sharing intimate body fluids with a person who has contracted the virus in this way is themselves at risk. And so is anyone having sex with them . . . and so on. It isn't who you are – gay, straight, bisexual; a drug-user or totally clean – it's what you do that puts you in the frame. And having unprotected sex is risk enough. So if you *are* having sex with a partner whose sexual history you cannot guarantee over the last ten years, wear a condom and use Safer Sex practices. If you don't, you may as well put a loaded gun to your head (*and* your partner's when you return home) and have done with it.

OPEN MARRIAGES

In open marriages one or both of the partners may openly have long-term or short-term affairs with other people. The argument here is the same as with affairs, but without the secrecy. Obviously, partners in an open marriage cannot be accused of deceit or lying to each other, but are they always honest to themselves and does it always benefit a relationship? Some say it does, but with others the enthusiasm for 'openness' can be one-sided. An open relationship can be seen as sexual infidelity dressed up with jargon – just a way of having extra-marital affairs without recrimination. The less eager partner may go along with the 'agreement', knowing that if they don't their partner will stray anyway, but in secret, or that they will leave the relationship. Interestingly, enthusiasts of open marriage are often very liberal about their own affairs but less keen on their partners having them. Sauce for the goose is not always sauce for the gander.

SWAPPING AND SWINGING

As swinging just means being sexually adventurous, you can swing in a stable relationship. More often, though, it is a word used together with swapping, or exchanging partners.

Swapping can involve group sex. That is, couples might meet at swapping parties and have sex with whoever takes their fancy. They can do this either in private in a separate room, or in public as part of the proceedings. Swapping may also involve two couples getting together for the purpose. Again they may have sex as a group or each couple might go off to separate rooms.

Swapping attempts to get round the emotional risks of extra-relationship sex, by making it a shared activity between the couple. Similarly, swapping parties keep the activity to a set time, so you can have sex without any emotional commitment. And swapping between couples becomes a four-way involvement, rather than each partner going off to have their own separate sexual relationship outside. But there are *still* emotional risks if one or other is going along to please or placate their partner, or if one enjoys the experience too much. And there are the physical risks, too.

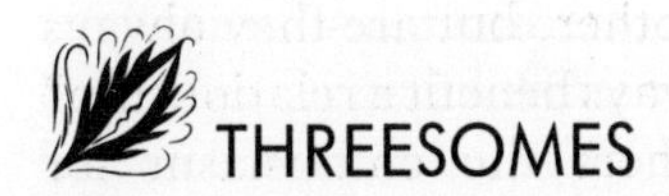

THREESOMES

Some couples find it exciting to involve someone else. The third person may be invited to have sex with one partner while the other looks on. The observing spouse may masturbate while watching, or wait until their partner and the guest have finished and then take their turn, with either of them. Or all three may have sex together. Threesomes can involve two men and one woman or two women and one man. They may, or may not, involve homosexual acts.

If the threesome is made up of two men and a woman, do remember that any sexual act between the two men will be illegal. This is because homosexual acts between consenting adult men are only legally allowed if they occur *in private*. The presence of the woman breaks this law. However if the threesome is between two women and a man, any sexual activity between the women would be legal. This is because the law does not even recognise the existence of female homosexuality!

If you want to try threesomes you could look around your own social circle to see if anyone else is equally keen. You could also look in the classified advertising section of specialist magazines. Before you proceed, however, it might be a good idea to discuss and perhaps even draw up an agreement. The same agreement could apply to open marriages.

The first move must be to talk the subject over with your partner, honestly and fully. If either of you has any reservations, you *must* think again. You will be risking both the relationship and your partner's emotional well-being (and possibly their physical well-being too) if you go ahead without agreement, or pressure them to give in. Sexual bullying is one of the worst kinds of abuse. If your partner cannot agree to what seems important to you, you have to consider which is more important – the relationship or satisfying these demands. If it is the former, then accept the limitation you might think it sets. If it is the latter, then take steps to end the relationship, with consideration and kindness.

If both of you truly agree, then you'll need to discuss the boundaries of your open marriage or other sexual activities. You might, for instance, agree that:

- You will always use condoms and Safer Sex practices with any other partner
- You will tell your partner if you are involved with someone else
- You will stop any outside relationship if it takes up more time or emotional energy than your permanent one

- You will stop all outside relationships if your partner has second thoughts

For an open marriage, or sexual activities involving other people, to work, both partners need to be responsible, careful and sensitive to each other's feelings and needs, as well as being concerned for and honest with their other sexual partners. You need also to think very carefully about your beliefs and behaviour if you have children. Don't forget that they cannot be kept in the dark.If you don't explain your activities, someone else is bound to tell them and they could well be subjected to rumours and pressure from outsiders who do not agree with your views or do not understand your beliefs and behaviour.

8
THINGS TEMPORAL

You can't expect your love life to be enjoyable and relaxed, let alone passionate, unless you make time for each other. The strongest desires can wilt under the daily demands of home, job, family and friends. If you want your loving to be fun, you will need to take some control over your life and sort out four elements in your relationship:

- The time you spend together
- The private space you have
- The amount and type of attention you give each other
- The money you are prepared to spend on yourselves

Many of us, particularly women, feel we have been put on earth for only one purpose – to serve and promote the well-being of others. Parents (again, mothers particularly) feel that their children must come first, and spending time and money on themselves is somehow wrong.

Generosity, care, attention and love are all gifts that we *should* offer others, and we certainly owe them to our children. But we also owe ourselves a share of these. Just as we shouldn't abuse and use our children, partners, family or friends for our own ends, neither should we make ourselves doormats for theirs. 'Selfishness' can be just another word for being generous to ourselves; whereas always putting your own needs aside can encourage the people you love and care for to become selfish and demanding.

Everyone benefits when you and your partner stake a claim on some time for each other. You'll have more love to give *them* if you spend some time and money on yourselves.

TIME

With only 24 hours in a day, how can you fit time to be together into a busy schedule that may include running a home, caring for a family, doing a job and seeing your friends? The answer is that you need to *make* time.

Why not . . . make a date?

Make time for each other in each week. Some couples actually make dates with each other. You can check the calendar at the beginning of each month or week and pinpoint evenings or days or hours when you can and *will* spend time together.

If you have a family, try to cluster their activities together. So, if one child has a special interest one evening or a Saturday morning, see if the others can find something of their own to do then, too. It wouldn't be fair to insist, but once *you* recognise that you have the right to private time, your family will see this too and will want to help.

Then, when everyone else is off your hands, you can take advantage of being together. You could spend the time just relaxing in each other's company, talking or reading or watching TV. Or you could do something you both enjoy –

some sort of sport or exercise or special hobby, or eating out or going to a cinema.

There's also nothing wrong in deciding when, where and how you are going to make love, and planning for the event. We tend to assume that, to be truly romantic, lovemaking must be spontaneous. Rubbish! We do plan ahead by dressing up or making sure our teeth are brushed and our underwear clean. But we try not to admit that sex is on our minds. The unexpected can be fun, but some of the best and most enjoyable experiences in life are carefully orchestrated. So don't feel that you are being calculating or cold if you and your partner say 'Let's make love on Saturday night.' Knowing you are going to do it means that every movement, every glance and every touch from the beginning of the day is part of the build-up.

The important thing is to make time when work and other commitments are put aside. All those 'important' issues we spend time on are often far less important than our relationship. What is the point of being flawlessly houseproud, a champion DIY enthusiast, or winning a promotion at work if keeping up such standards prevents you nurturing your relationship? Most of us would prefer having a little less shine on the ornaments or would put up those shelves a day or so later if it meant a chance to laugh and love together.

Having time to relax often means getting necessary chores organised and shared out evenly. If you and your partner both work, and if you have a family, it makes no sense whatsoever for Mum to do the chores on her own. Children brought up to expect their mothers to do all the shopping, cleaning, tidying, cooking, washing up and caring, grow up into demanding, selfish and incompetent brats. So put your foot down and get everyone to pull their weight. Even small children can make their beds, tidy their rooms and be responsible for putting their own dirty washing in the machine. If you added up the time you spent running round after the family each week, while they slumped in front of the TV, you would probably find it amounted to enough hours to work your way through several massages, a shared bath *and* an aphrodisiac feast!

As well as getting your day-to-day and week-to-week routine organised, give a thought to extended time off.

Why don't you . . . have a break?

Look carefully at weekends and holidays. We often have mixed feelings about time away from home. We tend to remember jaunts away as idyllic and trouble-free and think of them as the only time when we get to see the whole family together, without pressure or interruptions. But the memory is often better than the reality. You and your partner may differ over what makes the perfect holiday. One of you might favour sunbathing while the other prefers exploring places and meeting people. If adults differ amongst themselves, children have yet another agenda. They are often bored and sulky with adult choices and resentful at being taken away from their friends at home. Instead of being the romantic, relaxing idyll we imagined, holidays – with or without children – are often stressful and argumentative.

To get round these problems, try to work out what you all *want* from a holiday. What are your needs and desires? Some of these elements may clash. But when you've each worked out your own list of priorities you can discuss a compromise that means everyone gets some of what they want, and no one loses out completely.

One solution could be to have separate holidays. You might find that everyone benefits if the kids go off on activity holidays, with friends. Or if you link up with the parents of their friends and divide a two-week holiday between you – you take all the kids for a week and they do the same for the other week. That way, both sets of parents have some time on their own.

Another idea is to give everyone a chance to do what they want for part of the holiday. You can do this in two ways:

1 Give each person a day on which they can choose what everyone does. No grumbles are allowed, because you all have a go, turn and turn about.
2 One part of the day is set aside for everyone to go and do their own thing, meeting afterwards to share adventures and impressions over lunch or in the evening.

You may spend less time together, or less time doing exactly what you want, but the time you *do* share should be free of quarrels and disappointment.

One of the best ways to rediscover your partner and your love is to treat yourself to the occasional special break – a second honeymoon. This might be just a few days away, or an entire holiday. The idea is to budget for something you can afford (so that you won't worry or row about the expense); somewhere you both like (so you won't argue about the surroundings); something you both want to do (so you won't bitch about boring beaches or exhausting sightseeing). Go with the express intention of rediscovering the romance in your lives, and without any guilt over indulging yourselves. Take this book along and work your way through!

It's also a good idea to try something new. It's easy to get in a rut with holidays. Giving your comfortable routine a jolt can definitely revitalise your love life. Since most of us want to recharge our batteries, we often think that lying around and doing nothing is the best way to relax on holiday. But physical activity is actually very refreshing and can leave you feeling more relaxed than just lying around on the beach. Even if you gave up games when you left school, consider taking a break where you learn to climb, canoe, swim, pothole, windsurf, parachute, ski, sail, scuba dive, abseil, camp, orienteer, or anything else that takes your fancy.

What about . . . periods?

Of course, it tends to take some of the romance out of things if you find that your period comes right in the middle of your special holiday or private time with your partner. Fortunately, nowadays you can do something about it. Control over periods is one of the best side effects of using the combined oral contraceptive – the Pill. Even if you don't want it to be your main method of contraception, you can take the Pill, for a short or extended time, to let you choose when, and when *not*, to have that time of the month. You can now use the Pill to:

- Make sure your period *never* falls at a particular time, such as the weekend. If you or your partner has a job that keeps you apart during most of the week, this can be particularly helpful.
- Miss a particular period if you were going to bleed on a special day or during a special week.
- Cut down on the number of periods you have. This is especially helpful if you have painful periods or are anaemic.

A lot of people worry about the safety aspects of the Pill but research now seems to show that being on one of the new low-dose pills can actually be healthier than not being on the Pill. If you were absolutely 'natural' and didn't use any method of birth control, you would only have around 35 periods during your life. You would either be pregnant or breastfeeding the rest of the time. So the body isn't really designed to have the 400 periods a modern woman might experience.

Research has shown that some cancers are more likely in women whose bodies are exposed to the rise and fall of hormones produced when they are not pregnant. Having fewer cycles in which ovulation takes place can protect you from a range of diseases, and the Pill seems to offer protection against pelvic inflammatory disease, ovarian and endometrial cancers, rheumatoid arthritis, anaemia, period pain and some breast disease. The big advantage of being on the Pill is that in effect, your body thinks you are pregnant, and ovulation *doesn't* happen.

If you are already on the Pill, you may be able to go ahead

and miss a period on your own, by carefully following the plan given below. But it is always worth letting your doctor know what you intend doing. If you did decide to make this a regular pattern – for instance, taking four packets, one after the other, over a three-month stretch and only having four periods a year – you would need extra supplies,as you would be taking 19 instead of 13 packets a year. And if you aren't on the Pill, or if you're taking a type that isn't suitable, you will need to consult a doctor – either your own or one at a family planning clinic. Explain what you would like to do. Very few doctors these days would see this as a trivial request.

You will need to have been on the Pill for at least two months before you can use it to postpone your period. If you try this method after only a month, you may still get 'breakthrough' bleeding. And you must be using the right kind of pill. This will *only* work with the Combined Pill – the one that contains both oestrogen and progestogen. It also needs to be the 'fixed dose' pill – all the pills in the packet should be the same colour.

Take your pill as normal. When you reach the end of the packet you are using, don't have a seven-day break. Simply continue with another packet. Go on taking one pill a day, as usual, for as long as you want your period to stay away. When you want to restart your normal routine, finish the packet you are using and *then* have a seven-day break before beginning again.

You could stop that *extra* packet early. So, for instance, you might take 28 or 40 or any number of pills one day after another to keep your period at bay for a set length of time.

This can also allow you to move your period along in a week. If, for instance, you always bleed Thursdays to Tuesdays, and would rather keep the weekend free, you can take extra pills to make sure that, in future, your period always arrives on a Monday and finishes by Friday. The only important things to remember are that you must:

1 *Never* have *more* than 7 days between finishing one packet and starting the next one.
2 *Never* have *less* than 21 continuous days of pill-taking.

The real advantage of keeping to a strict regimen of taking two packets in full is that you will still be starting and finishing a packet on a particular day. If Friday has always been your 'finish' day and Saturday your 'start up' day, you're less likely to forget.

If you are taking one of the 'phased' pills, you may not be able to manipulate them in this way without a doctor's help. Phased pills have a different measure of hormones throughout the month, shown by the fact that the packet contains two or three sets of pills of different colours. You can't use them to postpone a period on their own. The pills at the beginning of a packet are lower in dose than those at the end, so going from one packet to another causes a sudden drop in hormones and can lead to bleeding.

Your doctor can give you a packet of pills of a higher dose to keep bleeding at bay for an extra three weeks. Or you can go from the end of one packet straight to the pills in the *last* section of a spare packet of phased pills – missing out the earlier, lower-dose pills. This will only postpone your period seven, 10 or 14 days (depending on the brand) but this may be enough for your purposes.

The progestogen-only Pill *cannot* be used in this way. But your doctor could put you on the Combined Pill for a short time, unless there were medical reasons preventing you from taking it.

SPACE

The space you have to yourselves is as important as the time you allow yourselves. One of the best sex aids is a good, strong bolt on the bedroom door. Even in a close family with young children, partners need privacy. It is important for you to be able to shut a door and *know* that no one is going to burst in. Obviously, in an emergency, you should be available, and equally obviously no one should feel locked out or rejected. But it is also important to be able to say 'This is our private area and we don't want to be disturbed.' One good way of getting home the message that anyone wanting to come in should knock and wait, is to offer the same sort of respect in return. If *you* knock and ask if you can come into your children's rooms, they are more likely to accept your asking them to do this, too. If all else fails, get that bolt!

Your own space may also be important if you have a family and you and your partner want to explore additions to your love life – special clothing, equipment and visual material, for instance. You are likely to want to keep these private, and it is very difficult to prevent children from peeping into drawers and wardrobes. However much you demonstrate your respect for their privacy and teach them not to invade other people's, children cannot really be expected to observe these rules until they are old enough to sympathise with and understand other people's feelings. Young children simply *cannot* do this, and until they reach middle to late teens, you would be better off relying on locks rather than threats and punishments.

Place isn't only important in terms of privacy. However much you try to keep your relationship fresh, it is easy to get stale when you are in the same old surroundings day after day. A new bedroom, new scenery – even if it's only the other side of the county – can start things up again. Trying something more adventurous at home – practising massage, pouring scented oil in a shared bath or using a vibrator – may be difficult because it's easy to feel awkward or embarrassed at trying anything new in a familiar situation. Going away somehow releases all these inhibitions. If you can't afford to take a break in a hotel or guesthouse, why not find a friend or relative living some distance away who would be prepared to swap homes for a weekend or longer?

ATTENTION

The amount and type of attention you give each other can make such a difference to your love life. In the early stages of a relationship most of us *do* spend more time and effort on pleasing each other. We call this sort of behaviour 'courtship' or 'courting' – the paying of kind, respectful and polite attention in order to woo with amorous or marital intention. We talk about 'honeymoons' – the first, sweet part of a marriage during which both partners care for and cherish each other. But this period is understood to be short-lived, a mere month, or 'moon', after the wedding, or beginning of the relationship. So, why do we stop trying once the honeymoon is over?

One reason could be the pressures put on men to live up to an idea of what is proper manly behaviour. From a very early age, boys are told that any show of feelings is unmanly and childish. A real man, the little boy is taught, does not cry. He does not show or talk about his feelings either. The only emotion he can show is anger. He can fight to his heart's content because aggression is a good, safe and acceptable masculine type of activity. Love is not.

When he's older, he can lavish care and gifts and even talk soppy to a woman, if it is for the purpose of getting her into bed. However, once she is won there is no more excuse. For a man to woo his steady girlfriend, his fiancée or his wife is entirely suspect and likely to call down scorn and criticism on his head from friends and even family. Boys grow up feeling that *touching* – anything from a stroke on the arm, through petting, stroking, hugging, to sensual and sexual massage – is dangerous or dirty, or just downright sissy. To climb on to your parent's lap and demand a cuddle, or snuggle up to your lover and ask for a hug, is to risk being sneered at.

The saddest part of this is that no one is happy with the result. In reality, men crave affection as much as women and would far rather continue 'courting' as long as the relationship lasts.

Plenty of men say they would like to take more time to kiss and cuddle at the beginning of making love. However, they are also more likely to think that intercourse is more important than kissing and cuddling. Whatever they *feel*, they *think* that getting straight to the main event as quickly as possible is the way to do it properly! So, next time you get together, why not slow down and see how long you can kiss and touch each other *before* having intercourse? See if delaying getting down to 'the real thing' makes it boring, or makes it better.

MONEY

You may be able to take holidays or breaks and buy each other little romantic gifts without worrying about the expense. But for most people there are always more items the household budget should stretch to cover than there are pennies to be stretched. Whether or not you have other family, it's often hard to spend money 'frivolously' on yourselves or each other without feeling that you are being irresponsible or selfish. But in most cases, what's really needed is sensible budgeting. If you think you can't afford that expensive bath oil, the romantic dinner for two or the weekend away, it could be worth looking at what else your money is going on. Cigarettes, convenience food, three or four nights a week at the pub? Are there ways you could trim your weekly spending, putting away the savings for a luxury blow-out on something you would really enjoy together?

9
THINGS SURGICAL

We have been using the surgeon's knife to try to change and improve our bodies, and thus our love lives, for centuries. Doctors as long ago as 600 BC, and as far away as India and China, removed excess breast tissue, corrected cleft lips, and improved abnormal scars.

Surgery may help us look better and so allow us to feel confident in approaching lovemaking. Or it may correct a physical problem that could otherwise make sex difficult or impossible.

Gynaecological problems can make sex painful, difficult, and unpleasant for women, and surgery *may* offer some relief here. Fibroids and ovarian cysts can cause pain on intercourse, as can endometriosis (a condition where cells that normally line the womb have migrated and grown elsewhere in the body).

You may find that doctors are reluctant to resort to surgery unless they feel it is medically justified. Some doctors might not consider sexual difficulty an important enough reason to justify surgery. However, this is a short-sighted view, since physical health and emotional well-being so often go together.

Similarly, men with prostate difficulties or a testicular problem such as varicocele (a painful varicose vein on the scrotum) might also be asked to wait for treatment until the condition affects their physical well-being seriously enough to warrant it on medical grounds, not because it interferes with their loving.

For both men and women, it can be worth pushing for immediate treatment on the grounds that what is good for your love life has to be good for you.

COSMETIC SURGERY AND BODY RESTRUCTURING

It's easy to understand why most of us have an obsession with our appearance. Love may conquer all, but everyone knows that looks make the world go round. The body beautiful is used to sell us everything from cars to wheelbarrows. At the same time we are sold the concept of what we *should* look like. The ideal body is tanned, slim and tall. The ideal woman has hair only on her head – not on her body – and has medium-sized, apple-shaped breasts with erect nipples. Her desirable mate has just the right amount of masculine body hair and an even, nicely shaped bulge in his pants. Short, hairy women with soft breasts and dimpled nipples, and skinny, bald men need not apply.

As we know, most of these media images are the result of all sorts of technical tricks, so don't think you need cosmetic surgery just because your body is nothing like the ones you see in the papers. However, there *are* cases when surgical help can be justified. If you've spent your whole life convinced that the shape of your nose, ears, breasts or genitals makes you a laughing stock, or actually causes you physical discomfort, no amount of persuasion may convince you otherwise. What can be done? There would seem to be no limit other than the amount you can afford to spend to have your body reshaped.

BREAST ENLARGEMENT

This is an operation to enlarge and firm up your breasts by inserting silicone, or polyurethane bags containing silicone gel or saline water, behind them.

A surgeon makes incisions underneath the breast, or in the armpit, or in the areola (the dark area around the nipple). The bags are placed either between the existing breast tissue and the muscle that lies against the ribs, or between muscle and ribs. The implant pushes out the woman's own natural breast tissue and can both look and feel perfectly normal. The same operation can be, and increasingly *is* done on men to give them muscular-looking 'pecs'.

Good and bad points

Breast implants don't stop a woman being able to breastfeed. They do not make her more likely to develop breast cancer and will not mask symptoms such as breast lumps. In most cases, the operation and the implants don't affect feeling in the breast. A breast operation can give enormous confidence to a woman who has previously felt lacking.

However, one in ten women suffer a loss of feeling in the nipples, although this may be recovered in the six months or so following the operation. In some women, scar tissue builds up around the bag, making the breasts hard and unnaturally regular in appearance. Implants can shift and silicone can leak from the bag into the body. An implant can shield underlying tissue during mammography. And some men, whose partners have had a little too much added to their measurements, describe making love to them as being like trying to enjoy yourself while lying on a concrete ramp!

INVERTED NIPPLES

If your nipples cannot or will not stand out even when stimulated, this operation will enable them to do so. The surgeon cuts through the areola (the darker area around the nipple) and separates the shortened milk ducts that pull the nipples flat against the surface or inside the breast.

Good and bad points

As with all cosmetic surgery, this operation can increase your confidence if you are distressed about your appearance. However nipples are not really meant to stand out except when stimulated. Many women who feel something is wrong with their nipples – or men who feel there is something wrong with their partner's nipples – only think this because of inaccurate images shown by the media. Surgery to make nipples stand out will *always* prevent your breastfeeding in the future and will reduce sensation to some extent. You may even be unlucky enough to lose it altogether. Is it worth it?

BREAST REDUCTION

As well as their ability to give, the cosmetic surgeons can also take away, and breasts or any other parts can be reduced in size. In this operation an incision is made in the lower half of the breast and excess tissue is removed. The nipple and the surrounding area are moved upwards, and the whole is sewn back together. For men with excess breast tissue, the incision is usually made in the areola.

Good and bad points

Big breasts are not always as sexy as some men and women think. As well as being embarrassing, they can be heavy and lead to a painful stoop or tender areas on the shoulders where bra straps dig in. The underside of a large breast can often be sore, red and smelly, where it lies against the chest and stomach. So breast reduction can be a great relief to many of the women who seek it – and just as much a relief for men who can also suffer from enlarged breasts.

On the other hand, breast reduction does stop any chance of breastfeeding and, in most cases, the nipples will be less sensitive.

LIPOSUCTION

This operation 'vacuums' unwanted fat from hips, thighs and elsewhere. The patient is put under general anaesthetic and a narrow tube is passed through the skin. Fat cells are then sucked out.

Good and bad points

The results can be surprisingly long-lasting and extremely useful for people who have found that no amount of genuine dieting can shift those last pounds. An interesting little side effect is that liposuction can apparently increase breast size. Doctors at Ohio State University report that as many as 75 per cent of women having liposuction from another part of the body developed larger breasts. So you *could* get a free breast job as well as prettier hips. The good news is that men do not seem to react in the same way!

But liposuction is really only suitable for some people and some parts of the body. It's definitely not an easy alternative to sensible eating and exercise.

LABIA RESTRUCTURING

Women can have an operation to reduce and tidy up the labia (the inner and outer fleshy lips on each side of the vagina). In cases where the labia are large enough and hang down far enough to be uncomfortable, they can be reduced in size. The excess tissue is cut and stitched to make this area smaller and neater.

Good and bad points

This can be a helpful operation for the very few women who suffer pain and discomfort from unusually large and hanging labia. But, although the ability to feel sensations is spread throughout this area, such an operation can reduce pleasure.

The problem with operations to the genitals is that they are sometimes done because a woman or her partner *thinks* her genitals are ugly or malformed, when they are actually perfectly normal. What perhaps should be altered is attitude. Either or both partners should be helped to come to terms with the fact that a woman's sexuality is every bit as red, fleshy and turgid as a man's.

Note

This operation and the following one should not be confused with infibulation and excision, also sometimes called 'female circumcision'. These are dramatic and disfiguring mutilations of the female genitals, still performed in certain cultures, sometimes without proper surgical skill or hygiene. In excision, the clitoris and all or part of the labia minora are cut away. In infibulation, the clitoris, the labia minora and part of the labia majora are cut away and the vaginal opening mostly stitched up. The aim is to keep women from having sex before marriage and to keep them faithful afterwards, by making sex a less appetising prospect. There is also a fear of women's genitals – the knife is felt to cleanse and beautify them.

These ritual operations are surrounded by centuries of belief and acceptance. Even women with relatives who have died as a result of it will insist on themselves and their daughters having the operation, knowing that otherwise they will be treated as outcasts.

FEMALE CIRCUMCISION

This is an operation to free the clitoris from any tissue that surrounds and fixes it, or removes part of the clitoral hood.

Good and bad points

Some women report greater sensitivity and feeling after a circumcision and both men and women may say they find the appearance of an exposed clitoris exciting. But, unlike the penis, the clitoris shrinks and retreats inside its protective fold of skin as orgasm approaches. Most women find the clitoris becomes so tender at this point that direct touch would be painful rather than pleasant.

As with *any* mutilating operation, any woman considering it, or man suggesting it, should look carefully at their motives. Trimming, reducing and tidying up are ways of cutting down to size and controlling female sexuality. Before you opt for surgery, might it not be possible to find a man who would be happy to celebrate your natural body, rather than accepting the view of one who says it is ugly?

HYMENOPLASTY

This operation uses skin grafts to replace the hymen or maidenhead, often seen as a sign of virginity.

Good and bad points

In some countries or cultures, female virginity is highly valued; women may become outcasts if they cannot produce 'proof' of virginity in the shape of a tight vagina and bleeding on a wedding night. For them, hymenoplasty can be literally a lifesaver. Some widowed or divorced women may also choose to take a later partner some semblance of virginity to re-enact a traditional bridal night, but with no illusions.

Sadly, however, hymenoplasty reaffirms some people's view that, while men can be 'studs' and sow their wild oats, women should be 'pure and unsullied' and that sexual exploration *does* sully and damage them. I don't agree.

MALE CIRCUMCISION

In this operation the foreskin – the loose skin covering the end of the penis – is surgically removed.

In some cultures, the foreskin is removed soon after birth, either by a surgeon or by a member of a religion or a society who is practised in the procedure. In other cultures, circumcision forms part of the coming-of-age ceremony when boys approach puberty and become accepted as men. Circumcision may also be offered for medical reasons, such as phimosis (difficulty in drawing back the foreskin) or paraphimosis (inability to return it over the glans once you have drawn it back). In both cases, circumcision is usually advised to solve the immediate problem and to prevent its likely recurrence.

Good and bad points

Circumcision is often seen as an aid to sexual pleasure. There are also arguments in its favour on health grounds. It appears that circumcised men are less likely to suffer cancer of the penis and some sexually transmitted diseases, and that their wives are less likely to suffer cancer of the cervix. Whether this is strictly because of the foreskin's removal, or to do with better hygiene and less sexual activity also found in such groups, we don't yet know.

However, many men feel that circumcision is a mutilating operation. They may resent their parents for having had it done to them and feel that it was a castrating and controlling action.

There are a lot of arguments about whether male circumcision affects lovemaking. Those in favour claim that the exposed glans becomes slightly less sensitive, allowing the man to make love for longer. But there is no evidence to show that this is so. It really has to be a matter of choice and personal taste.

CORRECTIVE SURGERY FOR WOMEN

There are some situations when surgical help might be necessary, not just to make lovemaking pleasant, but to enable it to happen at all.

HYMENECTOMY

The hymen, the fold of membrane that partly blocks off the vagina, is usually thin and flexible. It often stretches and breaks long before a girl first has intercourse – after self-exploration or tampon use. But in some girls the membrane is thick and tough, and first attempts at intercourse are very painful. If the membrane resists gentle attempts to loosen it, it can be separated with minor surgery.

Good and bad points

While some women find their first experience of intercourse pleasant and others find it painful to a degree, a few women find it virtually impossible. In such a situation, a hymenectomy might be suggested.

However, we do tend to place such a lot of emphasis on the pain and bleeding expected at the first experience of sex that many women approach early lovemaking in fear. They can tense up so much that intercourse *is* impossible. This is not because of an unbreakable hymen, but because fear makes their muscles go into spasm. In this situation, offering a hymenectomy raises false hopes and doesn't tackle the real problem.

CORRECTIVE SURGERY FOR MEN

Some male surgery can be essential and profoundly life-changing. Men who cannot have an erection, because of illness or physical handicap, may now be given a prosthesis (an implant) to help them do so.

PENILE PROSTHESES

There are a number of different types of prosthesis, but basically they fall into three main groups. The first, and simplest, consists of two silicone rods implanted in the penis. They are either hinged at the base or contain stainless steel or coiled silver wire to give a 'bendable' effect that allows the penis to hang down during normal activities. When an erection is wanted, the man or his partner simply straightens the penis.

The second group is more sophisticated. The penis is implanted with two hollow shafts, connected to reservoirs filled with fluid. Any pressure on the tip of the penis causes a pump to flood the shafts, making the penis stand up. As with the rod prosthesis, the operation to implant this is fairly simple.

The third group, and the Rolls Royce of the prosthesis

world, is the inflatable type. This consists of a pair of inflatable silicone cylinders which are placed in the shaft, a pump implanted in the scrotum and a reservoir buried behind the abdominal muscle. The three parts are connected by silicone tubing. You get an erection by squeezing the scrotal pump which then moves fluid from the reservoir into the cylinders in the shaft. The results are a very realistic, firm erection with some increase in length and girth of the penis. However, the inflatable prosthesis *can* break down and its very complexity means that there is always a possibility of mechanical failure.

Good and bad points

Impotence can be a devastating condition. Counsellors and sex therapists may point out that, in a loving relationship, penetration is not necessary for either partner to reach full satisfaction. But this is no comfort to someone who feels that the inability to maintain an erection not only robs the act of love of its most essential ingredient, it also robs him of status and his life of any meaning. If that *is* your problem it might well be worth talking to your doctor about a prosthesis or an aid. It might lift the spirits if nothing else.

But remember that the surgery involved in implanting any type of prosthesis will cause irreversible damage. A normal erection won't be possible again, so it is a step that must only be taken when there is no hope of non-surgical treatment working. You would also be advised to seek this sort of help through your GP. Prostheses are not cheap and not all private surgeons or clinics are saints. The same people who pressurise vulnerable women into ill-considered breast enhancements or 'nose jobs' may well take advantage of the equally vulnerable impotent man.

Although you should be able to have intercourse (and to orgasm, ejaculate and father children if you were able to do so before the implant), there is a price to pay. The rod types give you a permanent erection. You can bend this into a reasonable position during normal activities, but you will have a rigid and enlarged penis at all times. The inflatables will look better in a limp state and also seem more natural when erect, but even this is far removed from a naturally functioning erect penis.

PENIS ENLARGEMENT

For those men who can perform sexually but have wondered if a surgeon could make them 'better endowed', the answer as yet and for the forseeable future is no. Penis enlargement is not a surgical option.

Most men are brought up from schoolboy experiences and later reading to think that anything smaller than a French loaf and less than ramrod-straight when erect is abnormal or inadequate. 'Normal' penis size is anything between 7 and 11 cm when flaccid and 14 to 18 cm when erect. (For anyone whose penis has not yet gone metric, that's 2¾ to 4¼ inches and 5½ to 7¼ inches.)

The size you are when limp also has little to do with the size you are when excited. The smaller penis swells more than does the larger, and most end up around the same. This means that the inferiority-inducing limp 'whoppers' that all men have seen in the changing room are likely to be no more than average when it actually comes to bedtime. The main problem with assessing how well you measure up is that yours will always look smaller than theirs. This is because a cylindrical object always looks smaller if you look down on it rather than looking at it from the side or 'front on'!

Cosmetic surgery might seem to be the magic wand that cures all bodily ills and dissatisfactions. But it has a down side. You may have convinced yourself that the only reason for any of your social or sexual failures is your body. Altering your nose or breasts will not make you the life and soul of the party if you are still a wallflower. And while looking for your magical solution you risk falling prey to medical cowboys. Unbelievably, a doctor does not have to have any specialist qualifications to practise cosmetic surgery in Britain. There are practitioners and clinics galore who are far more interested in your money than in your physical or emotional well-being.

The only safe way to approach cosmetic surgery (after talking it over with a counsellor and/or carefully considering whether this *is* for you) is by referral to a reputable surgeon through your own GP.

10
THINGS ILLEGAL

On the whole, two adults can do what they want with each other as long as both consent and they are in private. There are exceptions, however, and some activities and certain additions to loving are illegal.

ILLEGAL ACTS

OBESENITY AND THE LAW

The law does not set out to stop you seeing, enjoying or even making your own pornography. The sole purpose of the Acts that relate to pornography is to prevent the *distribution* of obscene articles. You could buy raunchy but not totally explicit material from a shop, and the shopkeeper would not be breaking the law and neither would you. (But if he shows such material in the window, he could be contravening the Indecent Displays Act.)

However, if you asked for your purchases to be sent by post, *both* of you might be at fault – you for 'procuring' and the shopkeeper for 'sending' indecent material by mail. If you try to bring back unacceptable material from abroad, the material may be impounded and you may be prosecuted. You can even make your own totally explicit material and view it by yourselves. But if you try to pass it on to anyone else, you could be in trouble. So selling, hiring, lending or even giving obscene material can be illegal. The problem, of course, is defining exactly what *is* obscene.

According to the Obscene Publications Act, an article is 'obscene' if it 'tends to deprave or corrupt' persons likely to come into contact with it. And, in the Post Office Act, 'indecent' is defined as 'offending against the recognised standards of propriety'. It is an offence to send through the post a package enclosing any indecent or obscene article. The Post Office has the authority to open packages to check them. The Customs Consolidation Act forbids the importation of indecent and obscene articles, and gives HM Customs the duty and power to search and seize offending packages and luggage.

As we know, the problem with all this is that it's almost impossible to *know* whether any given item is obscene or indecent. Few juries are prepared to admit that a magazine or film 'tended to corrupt or deprave' them. And standards change. Material that twenty years ago would have been banned from 'normal' society can be seen every day on our television screens, magazines or advertising hoardings. Thirty years ago, *Lady Chatterley's Lover* was the subject of a court case and a witness was asked seriously 'Would you want your wife or servant to read this?' Today, it is a university text and even some schools include it on their reading list.

Since material you think is acceptable may be seen by a judge or jury as tending to deprave or corrupt, the best advice is not to sell, hire, lend, give away or import. And don't order or send by post anything that is explicit. Finally, don't expect anything you *can* order by mail to be explicit.

Commercial suppliers are well aware of the laws, and the item you receive will almost certainly be far more innocent than the description in the advertisements or catalogues.

ANAL SEX

Anal sex can be as pleasurable as vaginal sex. Both the anus and the vagina contain nerve endings that produce pleasing sensations when rubbed. And since the muscle that sweeps from the pelvic bone, past the clitoris and round the vagina, also stretches around the anus, sensations felt in anal sex can be transmitted to the clitoris.

Is anal sex safe?

You can't get pregnant from anal sex so some people feel it is 'safe' in that sense. But, no, it isn't very safe in a medical sense because bacteria that live quite happily and usefully in the back passage can play havoc if transported elsewhere. If any matter – waste matter or body fluid – is carried on fingers or penis from the back passage to the water passage, it can set up nasty infections. So you should never let any part of you that has touched the back passage come into contact with mouth, vagina or urethra.

The back passage is also less flexible and more fragile than the vagina. The vagina is designed to stretch to let a baby emerge as well as to let any size of penis enter. In contrast, the most the back passage is normally supposed to encounter is a soft motion. So anal intercourse can result in tiny tears or wounds in the entrance and in the interior walls. These can be painful and take some time to heal and can also allow sexually transmitted diseases to enter the bloodstream. This is why infection by HIV (the virus that can cause AIDS) is such a risk with anal sex.

Is anal sex legal?

Amazingly, anal sex is still illegal between heterosexual couples even if they are consenting and in private, and even if they are married. The basis of the law is that, in matters sexual, the penis has one function, and one only. That is, it's there to be used for reproductive purposes. So masturbation is believed to be dangerous and homosexual acts to be wrong. Not much can be done about private acts of masturbation, and civil rights and changing views have done much to alter both laws and attitudes about homosexuality. But this strange state of affairs still remains, that putting the penis in a woman's rectum instead of in her vagina is an illegal act. You can insert vibrators, candles, bananas and even bottles as far as the law is concerned, and as long as you are both happy, but no amount of consent will legally let you use the male organ. So, be warned.

If you are prepared to go against the law, and the warnings in this book, and have anal sex, then at least protect yourself from infection. Use a condom and a spermicide, and make absolutely sure that nothing that comes into contact with the back passage is allowed to touch any other part of your own or your partner's body.

Homosexual anal sex

Anal sex *is* allowed between consenting men who are over the age of 21. However, it must be 'in private'. Behaviour that would be accepted by the law as being discreet in the case of heterosexuals is not considered so for gay people. For homosexuals to achieve legally safe privacy, they would probably have to go beyond not having anyone else in the room or in sight. A hotel room, for instance, even if the door were locked, might not be considered private, since there were other people in the same building. Neither would a room in a private house where other people were under the same roof. Theoretically, allowing gay friends to stay and to share a bedroom, or visiting them, could put *all* of you outside the law. The law really is an ass at times.

FORCE AND THE LAW

Any sexual act that would otherwise be legal can become illegal if consent is withdrawn. Until recently, the only person not protected by this was the married woman. Fortunately, the law is becoming less of an ass and beginning to accept that rape and abuse do occur within marriage. So having once said 'I do' may no longer mean that a woman gives rights of sexual access for all time.

Communication between couples is essential if you are to avoid sexual misunderstandings and keep the policeman out of your bedroom. It is not enough to think, feel, consider or assume that your partner is happy to go along with what you want sexually. Keep talking and sharing your emotions and your desires and never be afraid or too embarrassed to call a halt. And don't hesitate to walk away if your partner shows any signs of ignoring your reservations or not caring how you feel.

AGE AND THE LAW

As has already been stated, the suggestions and explanations offered in this book are intended for adults, to use on their own or with an equally adult partner who is also of an age to give valid consent. It is illegal for a man to have sex with a woman if she is under 16. Even if she *is* keen, in law she is not deemed old enough to say yes. The law was originally intended to protect young girls against being sold into prostitution to older men. Therefore, there is a sliding scale of seriousness for the offences of having sex with the under-aged.

If the girl is under 13 and the man over 25, he is more at fault than if she is between 13 and 16 and he is under 25. Same-age young lovers are seldom brought to court.

Sexual abuse by older men is now viewed seriously by the law, although often not as seriously and not as rigorously pursued as it should be. If they have any decency, men should take the lesson contained in this law seriously. It is irrelevant to point out that young girls are sexually aware and may both seek out and encourage sexual experimentation. When there is a gap in age, there is abuse, and the greater maturity and authority of the older man means that the younger girl cannot have real choices. Neither can she have the control that every person must have in a sexual relationship if it is to be truly loving and constructive.

If your taste is for lovers much younger than yourself, you have only two reasonable, civilised options:

1 Play-act with a mature and consenting partner and keep your tastes *strictly* within the realms of fantasy.
2 Seek counselling to understand your tastes and control your behaviour (see the organisations listed under Useful Addresses, pages 171–2).

ILLEGAL ADDITIONS

DRUGS

Drugs which are illegal, or are illegal if used for pleasure rather than as prescribed medicine, are often touted as sex aids. Users will tell you that making love while under the influence of cocaine, cannabis, hallucinogens, barbiturates or amphetamines makes the experience better. But medical professionals, who don't have the users' need of a self-justifying excuse, believe that drugs and sex make poor bedfellows.

The difficulty in attempting to describe the effect of illegal drugs is that they can vary so much from one individual to another. Some people can use and abuse with little or no effect; some can become dependent on them very quickly; some can give up; and others can become life-long addicts. So any description of the effects and consequences of drug use can only be in the broadest terms. All of the drugs whose misuse can be illegal do, however, work in one of three basic ways: as 'uppers,' 'downers' or 'hallucinogens'.

Uppers, like cocaine and amphetamines, speed up the body's reactions, heighten physical sensations and give a short-lived sense of boundless energy and physical power. The price paid for this 'high' is that it is followed by an equally strong 'low' of feeling miserable and ill at ease. The temptation is to relieve this discomfort by taking further doses of the drug. This produces the cycle that can lead to heavier misuse, in much the same way as unwise drinking followed by the old 'hair of the dog' remedy can eventually lead to alcoholism.

If the first group of drugs puts you 'up', drugs like heroin and the barbiturates are deliberately used to produce a 'down' feeling. They have the effect of slowing down sensations, taking the sharp edges off life and producing a protective 'being on a cloud' sensation. Barbiturates are the most dangerous of the abused drugs. Like the much higher-profiled heroin, barbiturates are often dissolved in water and injected. But, unlike heroin, they do not dissolve fully and can cause obstructions in veins. They can have fatal results if taken with alcohol; they are also the most difficult of all the drugs to withdraw from.

Cannabis and the hallucinogens are the perception-changers. Under their influence, the user can seem to hear, see, touch or taste in a way that appears far better than with his 'sober' senses. The danger is that the nature of these new perceptions depends on the emotional state of the drug-taker. These new sensations can just as easily be terrifying as enjoyable.

Most drug-taking that progresses beyond 'trying it once' can lead to what is called 'tolerance'. This is when the body gets used to the chemical and requires a bigger dose each time to get close to the original sensation. This 'ramp' effect is one-way, and once you are on it, it becomes difficult to go back. The real irony is that no matter how much you take, you never quite get back to the same high as the first, and frequently the best, experience. If you don't get off at this stage, you fly off the top of the ramp and fall into true addiction. At this point the body *must* have the drug to function at all and the drug is taken simply to ward off the painful symptoms its absence would produce.

STEROIDS

If you are keen on developing the body beautiful using some of the methods described in Chapter 4, you might have been tempted to use anabolic steroids. These protein-building drugs build tissue, strengthen bones and help muscles to recover quickly from injury. They can be taken to help increase staying power when doing weight-training or any other athletic exercise. They encourage muscle growth which can help both men and women achieve powerful and trim bodies. Steroids also increase aggression which can be seen as a benefit in sporting competitions or just in chasing personal goals. And such aggression can spill over into your sex life, making it more exciting and rampant.

Steroids mimic the effects of male hormones such as testosterone, which is why they encourage muscle bulk, aggression and sexual interest. However, if they are taken for these reasons over a period of time, they also encourage liver tumours and damage to the adrenal glands. Men may then find that after an initial upsurge, their sexual interest declines. They can become infertile and impotent, and their sex organs can shrink. Women who take steroids can find themselves becoming masculinised, with a deeper voice, more body hair and an increase in the size of the clitoris. In both sexes, the feelings of aggression can get out of control and create social arguments and difficulties. Steroids are now controlled drugs, and are not legally available without a doctor's prescription.

Warning

Whether legal, illegal or borderline, drug-assisted sex highs are not worth the temporary, permanent or even fatal side effects they can produce. Any initial amazing sexual spice or increased performance is soon replaced by diminished desire and often, ironically, male impotence. Unless you have the iron self-control (not usually a characteristic of drug-users) to keep your drug-use occasional and light, you very rapidly come to the point where you choose drugs *over* sex. The joys of the bed become a faint memory in an increasingly confused brain. And it is significant that 'It's better than sex. It's better than any orgasm' is a commonly heard, self-justifying excuse from addicts whose habit is out of control.

Recreational use of any of these drugs is illegal. So, as well as the risks to your physical, emotional and financial well-being, you would be doing something for which you could be arrested and convicted if ycu use them. There are so many other ways of spicing up, extending and diversifying your sex life. Unless you have a deep-seated need to punish or even kill yourself, there is simply no *need* to bother with things illegal. Stick to the items described in other chapters and, as far as things illegal are concerned, leave well alone.

A Note About Contraception and Safer Sex

CONTRACEPTION

In choosing a method of contraception,, you need to work out which one suits both of you best. What do you and your partner most want from your chosen method? Absolute protection from pregnancy? Total freedom to be spontaneous? A measure of protection from various forms of cancer or sexually transmitted disease? An absence of side effects or health risks? Freedom from a flow of vaginal secretions afterwards? A method that isn't going to get in the way of any sex aids you might want to try? A method that can *be* a sex aid, itself? To use any method efficiently, you need to be comfortable, and any distaste or lingering fears about your method of contraception is likely to end in disaster.

Having made a choice, you may find that your circumstances change. What was right at one time may no longer be best for you now. There are times in your life when it is more important that you avoid pregnancy. There are other times when you are dithering over whether or not to become pregnant and might welcome the opportunity to let chance or Nature take a hand. As you age, methods that might have been unacceptable due to lack of confidence or embarrassment become easy. Methods that might have been risky become safer as your fertility declines.

Many couples may find that they use a condom at first, for protection against sexually transmitted diseases and cervical cancer as well as pregnancy. Then they might move on to the Pill for a few years until they have their first child, using the cap just before a planned pregnancy and the IUD in the intervals between children.

After completing their family, they may mix diaphragm or cap, condom and sponge for a few years before deciding on sterilisation. They may still keep a supply of condoms and sponges as a back-up in case any of the other methods fail, for outdoor use at any time, or for specific occasions. Vibrator-users may find the diaphragm unsuitable, if the device is put inside the vagina. If you like scented oils, you can't use a male condom with them because they rot the rubber. And ticklers and IUDS may be incompatible – the IUD strings may get tangled with the device!

SAFER SEX

Being married, being in love and being clean are no protection against sexual infections. Contrary to the myths, infection with HIV, the virus that can cause AIDS, is *not* confined to homosexual men, drug-abusers and their partners. You aren't only at risk of getting a sexual infection if you belong to a group that has been described as high-risk, such as gay men or injecting addicts who share needles. It isn't membership of such a group that puts you at risk, but any involvement in high-risk activities. And simply having sex with someone who has been exposed to such a risk is in itself risky.

You, your partner, your partner's former lovers and *their*

former lovers may all have been heterosexual and never used drugs. But *one* contact somewhere back along the line could have introduced HIV. You could have HIV for years without knowing and before symptoms began to show. So, unless you and your partner have had no other sexual contacts for ten years or have had a negative test for HIV more than six months after your last sexual contact, you *could* be at risk. And if either of you does have other sexual contacts, the risk remains.

There are three ways of making sure HIV or any other sexual infection stays out of your relationship:

1 Only ever have sex with one partner who is equally faithful.
2 If you have had sex with anyone less than ten years ago, have a check-up and then stay faithful to each other.
3 Practise Safer Sex.

HIV is carried in body fluids – semen, vaginal wetness and blood. It has also been found in *very* small quantities in saliva and tears. The expert opinion is that, since the virus is actually quite fragile, it dies before passing on to anyone through swallowing or inhaling. There is no proof that anyone has ever caught the virus from contact with saliva or tears – only through getting semen, vaginal fluid or blood into their own bloodstream. So Safer Sex means avoiding sexual behaviour that could make this transfer of fluids possible. Instead, you can enjoy giving and receiving pleasure in low-risk sexual activities.

High-risk sexual activities

These include any activity that puts body fluids into intimate contact. The most dangerous would be anal intercourse, followed closely by vaginal intercourse. Anal intercourse can result in minute tears and wounds in the back passage, giving easy access to the bloodstream for any infection in the semen of the penetrator. Vaginal sex allows semen to pool and lie against the neck of the womb. The skin covering this area is very thin and delicate and can let infection penetrate. *Any* act that draws blood and allows it to come into contact with vulnerable areas, cuts or grazes can be high-risk.

Lower-risk sexual activities

Oral sex, sharing sex toys and using hands and fingers on the genitals can be risky, although they are slightly safer than high-risk sex.

Low-risk sexual activities

Using, but not sharing, sex toys, massaging and masturbating yourself or each other, kissing, and penetrative sex using a condom are all low-risk.

No-risk sexual activities

Solo masturbation, 'talking dirty', fantasising, using a vibrator or sex toy by yourself, and massage and body rubbing without touching genitals, don't involve any risk.

As I hope this book shows, there are many ways you can please each other and yourself *without* putting penis in vagina, and without sharing or passing body fluids. Penetrative sex is not the be-all and end-all of joyful, loving and exciting sex. In fact, it can often be a distraction. If you confine yourselves to penetration, you may miss out on all the other extra ways you could stroke, rub, caress and tease each other to happy satisfaction. Safer Sex can allow you to relearn how to fully please each other.

USEFUL ADDRESSES

One depressing aspect of sex aids in this country is the sleazy way they are presented and advertised. The specialist shops are often unattractive, and the mail-order catalogues can be too lurid for comfortable use. What could and should be fun becomes furtive, and embarrassment can hold people back from obtaining goods in which they have a genuine interest.

In America there are mail-order services which are very different. They are run by women for women and their catalogues really show the difference that good, non-sensational presentation can make. Perhaps manufacturers in this country could take a leaf out of their books? They would *have* to if more people ordered from the States than from them. Since the American products often cost less, it could be worth ordering goods from them, despite the additional postage.

Having read this book you may like to contact some of the companies or organisations listed below. With the exception of the helping agencies, I do not necessarily recommend or approve any of the listed services. Since this book is for adults, I also assume that any reader takes responsibility for reading it, and for any action that proceeds from having read it. Don't complain if anything said in these pages or anything you obtain from any of the addresses listed here shocks you. YOU DON'T HAVE TO LOOK!

General Suppliers

The following are some of the larger suppliers of a wide range of sex toys, underwear, videos, pills and potions. Some will charge for their catalogues, with the amount refundable against any purchase. They all offer a confidential and discreet service, and most will accept credit cards if you want to avoid cheques payable to 'Naughty Nighties' or such passing through your bank. With the exception of the American company, their literature tends to be somewhat explicit and sensational.

Ann Summers Ltd, Gadoline House, 2 Godstone Road, Whyteleafe, Surrey CR3 OEA. Tel: 081 660 0102

Lovecare, 328 Oxford Road, Reading, Berks RG3 1AF

Yago Holdings Ltd, Unit 18, Roman Way, Coleshill Industrial Estate, Coleshill, Birmingham B46 1RL

Magic Moments, 14 Rock Close, Hastings, East Sussex TR35 4 JW. Tel: 0424 853366

Private Lines, 627 Forest Road, London E17 4NE. Tel: 081 534 8855

Eve's Garden, 119 West 57th Street, Suite 420, New York,NY 10019, USA

Clothing and Equipment Suppliers

The specialist suppliers of fetish and fantasy clothing in rubber, plastic or leather usually produce far better-quality goods than the 'novelty' clothing items obtainable from the more general companies. Many items can be made to measure or to a customer's own designs or requirements. Most of the catalogues are glossy, beautifully illustrated and expensively produced. They are usually only sent for a charge which is refundable against any purchase.

Rubber, Plastic and Leather Clothing

Una Deva, PO Box 1177, Cheddar, Somerset BS27 3UQ. Tel: 0749 870611

She-An-Me, PO Box 171, Gerrards Cross, Bucks SL9 7NE. Tel: 075366 2000

Skin Two, 23 Grand Union Centre, Kensal Road, London W10 5AX. Tel: 081 968 9692

Mode Inc Ltd, 451 Roman Road, London E3 5LX. Tel: 081 980 1365

Mainly for Men

Feitico, Wylye Court, 48 Park Lane, Salisbury, Wilts SP1 3NS. Tel: 0722 323452

Fantasy Erotique, 7 Disraeli Road, London E7 9JR. Tel: 081 555 2996

Zipper, 283 Camden High Street, London NW1 7BX. Tel: 071 284 0537

Bondage

Hidebound, PO Box 10, Liverpool L36 6LD. Tel: 051 480 2443

She-An-Me (See above)

Sexy Underwear

The best made and most luxurious underwear in silk, satin and other delicious materials probably comes from companies who wouldn't be seen dead advertising in a sex magazine. However, they would be less than honest if they didn't admit that their products are meant to be seen and touched as well as worn.

For both sexes, try:

Shamian, 50 High Street, Hinton, Charterhouse, Bath BA3 6AN. Tel: 0225 722009

For female luxury, try:

David Nieper, Saulgrove House, Dept CL01, PO Box 14, Somercotes, Derby DE55 4QW. Tel: 0773 836000

Body Jewellery, Tattooing and Body Piercing

For the most complete range of body ornaments, and advice on reputable and safe tattooing and piercing, contact:

Body Jewellery, Blake House Studios, Blake End, Rayne, Braintree, Essex CM7 8SH. Tel: 0376 550020

Oils and Herbs

Many of the oils, essential oils, herbs and spices mentioned in this book can be obtained by mail order from:

Neal's Yard Apothecary, 2 Neal's Yard, London WC2. Tel: 071 379 7222

Hartwood Aromatics, 12 Station Road, Hatton Warwick, Warwicks CV35 7LG. Tel: 0926 842873

G Baldwin and Co, 171 – 173 Walworth Road, London SE17. Tel: 071 703 5550

John Bell and Croyden, 52–54 Wigmore Street, London W1H OAU. Tel: 071 935 5555

The Body Shop, Hawthorn Road, Wick, Littlehampton, West Sussex BN17 7LR. Tel: 0903 717107

Magazines

The advertisements in specialist magazines are often the best way of finding out what is available for any particular interest. They can also be a way of contacting other devotees should you want to.

Body Art covers all aspects of body adornment and is published four times a year by Body Art, Blake House Studios, Blake End, Rayne, Braintree, Essex CM7 8SH.

"O" is a magazine for the rubber or plastic clothes fancier. It usually has four issues a year and is obtainable from Una Deva (see page 169).

Forum is probably the oldest UK sex magazine. It contains everything from readers' fantasy letters to serious medical articles, as well as offering a panel of experts who will answer *any* sexual query. The magazine is published monthly and is widely available through most newsagents. Or direct from:

Northern and Shell PLC, Northern and Shell Building, PO Box 381, Mill Harbour, London, E14 9TW. Tel: 071 987 5090.

Problems

The first step with any sexually related problem – physical or emotional – should be to go to your own GP. He or she might have relevant training in this field. If not, they should be able to refer you on to specialist help. If counselling is suggested, or you think this could be the answer, advice on how to contact your nearest suitable counsellor can be obtained from:

Relate, Herbert Gray College, Little Church Street, Rugby CV21 3AP. Tel: 0788 573241 (or see the phone book for your local branch)

British Association for Counselling, 1 Regent Place, Rugby, Warwicks CV21 2PJ. Tel: 0788 578328/9

Family Planning Association (see *Information* opposite).

Information, support and help with physical disability and sexuality can be had from:

SPOD (The Association to Aid the Sexual and Personal Relationships of People with a Disability), 286 Camden Road, London N7 0BJ.
Tel: 071 607 8851/2

Advice on sexual orientation, gender difficulties, transvestitism or trans-sexuality can be had from the following three agencies. It must be stressed that these are serious, professional advisory organisations. They will *not* attempt to influence your final choice of sexual direction.

Beaumont Society, BM Box 3084, London WC1N 3XX

Gender Disphoria Trust, BM Box 7624, London WC1N 3XX.

Gay Switchboard. Tel: 071 837 7324 (or see the phone book for your local branches)

Information or help with anything related to HIV or AIDS can be obtained from:

Terrence Higgins Trust. Tel: 071 242 1010

National AIDS Helpline. Tel: 0800 56 123 (freephone)

Information

For help and advice and leaflets on any aspect of contraception, reproductive and sexual health, or for addresses of clinics and other services, contact:

Family Planning Association, 27 – 35 Mortimer Street, London W1N 7RJ. Tel: 071 636 7866

For leaflets on general health, healthy eating, exercise and Safer Sex, contact:

Health Education Authority, Hamilton House, Mabledon Place, London WC1H 9TX. Tel: 071 383 3833

FURTHER READING

The Kama Sutra Vatsyayana. Translated by Burton (Hamlyn 1987)

The Perfumed Garden Shaykh Nefzawi. Translated by Burton (Panther 1982)

Making Love Michael Castleman (Penguin 1988)

Treat Yourself To Sex Paul Brown & Carolyn Faulder (Penguin 1989)

Making The Most of Loving Gill Cox and Sheila Dainow (Sheldon Press 1988)

Making The Most Of Yourself Gill Cox and Sheila Dainow (Sheldon Press 1988)

Becoming Orgasmic Julia Heiman and Joseph LoPiccolo (Piatkus 1988)

The Woman Book of Love And Sex Deidre Sanders (Sphere Books 1985)

The Woman Report On Men Deidre Sanders (Sphere Books 1987)

The Hite Report Shere Hite (Summit books 1977)

The Hite Report On Male Sexuality Shere Hite (Optima 1990)

The Kinsey Institute New Report On Sex June Reinisch and Ruth Beasley (Penguin 1990)

Contraception John Guillebaud (Pitman 1985)

Safer Sex Diane Richardson (Pandora 1990)

Cosmetic Surgery Denise Winn (Optima 1989)

The Counselling Handbook Susan Quilliam and Ian Grove-Stephensen (Thorsons 1990)

Sexual Exercises For Women Anthony Harris (Quartet Books 1985)

The Magic Of Massage Ouida West (Century Publishing 1983)

The Complete Book Of Massage Clare Maxwell-Hudson (Dorling Kinderlsey 1990)

Super Massage Gordon Inkeles (Piatkus 1989)

Aromatherapy Danièle Ryman (Piatkus 1991)

Aromatherapy Judith Jackson (Dorling Kindersley 1990)

The Foods Of Love Max de Roche (Dorling Kindersley 1990)

My Secret Garden: Women's Sexual Fantasies Nancy Friday (Quartet Books 1988)

Men in Love: Their Secret Fantasies Nancy Friday (Arrow Books 1989)

INDEX

Page numbers in italics refer to illustrations

About the Author

SUZIE HAYMAN is a full-time freelance journalist, author and broadcaster. Before turning freelance she worked for both the Family Planning Association and the Brook Advisory Centres. She is on the National Executive Committee of the FPA and the Board of Brook Advisory Centres.

Suzie has written for numerous national magazines and newspapers, including *Bella, Woman, Prima, Good Housekeeping* and *The Guardian*. She is agony aunt of *Essentials* magazine, and also of *Who Cares?* – the National Children's Bureau's magazine for young people in care. Suzie has a fortnightly phone-in programme with Robbie Vincent on LBC radio. She also appears regularly on television.

Suzie has written several other books, including *It's More than Sex: a survival guide to the teenage years, Living with a Teenager* (published by piatkus), *The Well-Woman Handbook* and *Vasectomy and Sterilisation.*

She lives in a 300-year-old Cumbrian farmhouse with her partner Vic, and three cats.